Mary McLeod Bethune

Girl Devoted to Her People

Illustrated by James Cummins

Mary McLeod Bethune

Girl Devoted to Her People

By Olive W. Burt

THE **BOBBS-MERRILL** COMPANY, INC.
A SUBSIDIARY OF **HOWARD W. SAMS & CO., INC.**
Publishers • INDIANAPOLIS • NEW YORK

For Elizabeth Fortune,
who, like Mary Jane McLeod, has an
eager desire to learn

Illustrations

Full Pages

	PAGE
"Here's a snake," she screeched.	31
"Let us sing," he said.	53
"I want to learn how to read!"	69
Mary Jane began to sing.	80
Mary Jane felt right at home.	102
They liked to hunt spring flowers.	127
"What's the South coming to?"	143
"I'm certain that I'll need help."	167
The children filed into the room.	181
She had a special affection for her study.	191

Numerous smaller illustrations

Contents

PAGE

A Birthday for Janie 11

Danger in the Cotton Patch 23

Why Can't I Read? 35

Fear in the Night 44

A Promise Is Made 56

The Cotton Is Sold 71

A Gift for Janie 82

Off to School 92

PAGE

Mary Jane Leads Out 105

Learning and Sharing 115

Reading Proves Worthwhile 131

Graduation Day 146

Another Chance 159

A School by a City Dump 172

Friend of Presidents 183

Books by Olive W. Burt

CHIEF JOSEPH: BOY OF THE NEZ PERCE
JED SMITH: YOUNG WESTERN EXPLORER
JOHN ALDEN: YOUNG PURITAN
JOHN WANAMAKER: BOY MERCHANT
LUTHER BURBANK: BOY WIZARD
MARY McLEOD BETHUNE: GIRL DEVOTED TO HER PEOPLE
THE RINGLING BROTHERS: CIRCUS BOYS

Mary McLeod Bethune

Girl Devoted to Her People

A Birthday
for Janie

"WHAT'S A BIRTHDAY, Grandma? What's a birthday?" Mary Jane McLeod came running into the
kitchen where her grandmother sat rocking by
the big, black iron stove.

It was a late afternoon in July, in the year
1884, in Sumter County, South Carolina. Mary
Jane, a healthy little girl of about nine, was panting from running. She squatted on the low stool
beside her grandmother and stared up into the
wrinkled face. Grandmother Sophie had always
been able to answer Mary Jane's questions, and
this was something the little girl just had to find
out right away.

Sophie stopped rocking and looked down at her little granddaughter. "What questions you ask, Janie! What's your birthday? Why, that just means the day you were born."

"When's my birthday, then?"

"The day you were born, child? I recollect that day, I surely do. It was cotton blossoming time, just like now. The cotton patch was all bright and gay with flowers. You were a homely little thing—black as my grandchild ought to be, but with eyes asking questions as soon as they saw daylight. Now, tell me why you are asking about your birthday."

"Because I want to have a party on my birthday. That's why I'm asking."

"Goodness, child! Whatever put such a notion as that into your head? Birthdays and birthday parties are for white folks. When I was a field hand owned by the Wilsons, I saw many a birthday party. The guests came all decked up in pretty clothes, and there were fancy flowers and a cake. But black folks can't have any such frills as all those things."

"Well, I plan to, Grandma, if you'll just tell me when my birthday is."

"What's this I hear?" jeered Mary Jane's brother Willie. "I can just see you having a birthday party! Are you going to invite me?"

Willie had followed Mary Jane into the room and stood, feet wide apart, listening to his sister. He was two years older than Mary Jane and liked to tease her, but they were good friends just the same.

"What put this birthday party notion into your head, Janie?" asked Grandmother.

Willie answered before Mary Jane had a chance. "When we took the wash back to the white folks today, that girl Louise was having a birthday party. She gave us pieces of her cake. When we came away, Janie said she was going to have a birthday and a birthday party of her own. She always wants to do what white girls do."

"Such selfish feelings are sinful, child. Black folks are mighty lucky to be free. Your father and mother work hard, and you have far more than most colored folks." She raised her eyes toward heaven in grateful thanks.

Mary Jane said softly, "I know, Grandma, I'm thankful to be free, but if I'm free, why can't I have a birthday party? Just tell me when my birthday is. Louise knows hers."

"Yes, Louise is about your age. You two were born just about the same time. Your mother used to carry you up there to get the wash, and Louise was a baby, too. Now stop begging. Hattie is crying. Go and bring her here."

Mary Jane went into the small bedroom and picked up her year-old sister. She brought her and placed her on the old woman's lap.

"The sun is almost down," said Grandmother.

14

"Did that birthday party keep you from returning sooner? Your mother will be put out because you didn't get back in time to chop some weeds. The whole family has been out in the cotton patch, chopping weeds, while you and Willie were eating cake at a party."

"We can go now, Grandma!"

"It's too late. You would have to turn around and come back as soon as you get there. Just go and sweep up the yard, and Willie, you fill up the woodbox for your mother."

The two children went outside. Mary Jane picked up the old brush-broom used in the yard and started to work. Her brother went out to the woodpile at the back of the cabin. "I guess we shouldn't have mentioned the party today," Mary Jane said, "but I just couldn't forget that big pink mountain of cake."

She picked up a rock and slammed it into the grapevine that covered one end of the cabin. The fruit was a wonder to her—each bunch, each tiny grape perfect in shape.

"Well, I'm still going to have a birthday party," she declared. "If Louise and I were born about the same time, I'll just choose today for my birthday, too."

She started to plan how she could celebrate her birthday. Of course she couldn't have a pink mountain of cake like Louise's, but she could have a make-believe cake! She began to look for acorns from the old oak tree that shaded the cabin, but she couldn't find many. Snooty, the sow that had been turned out to forage, had eaten most of the acorns on the ground. But here and there the sow had missed a few acorns that the wind had blown into tiny pockets.

Mary Jane forgot her work. She gathered all the acorns she could find and began to pound them between two stones. Willie came back around the cabin with his arms full of wood.

16

"What are you doing?" he asked.

"I'm making me a birthday cake."

Willie took the wood inside and came back. "That won't look like a real birthday cake," he said. "Who would want a slice of that?"

"I haven't asked you to have a share!" said Mary Jane. "Anyway, this cake is not for eating. It's just for looking at." She took the pasty stuff in her hands and began to pat it into a little round cake.

"You might invite Snooty," said Willie. "She would enjoy eating your old cake."

Mary Jane giggled. "That would make it a real party! Can you bring old Snooty?"

Willie was happy because his sister had accepted his suggestion. "I'll try," he said, and galloped away to the pigsty.

From the fence he grabbed a long tattered rope which was used for leading Old Bush, the mule. He fastened one end of the rope around the sow's neck and gave her a nudge with his bare toes. "Get up, Snooty! Get up!" he cried. "You're going to a party."

Snooty wasn't interested in parties. She preferred to lie in the mud. "Get up!" cried Willie, again giving the sow a kick.

The old sow got to her feet, but even though he pulled and tugged with all his might, he couldn't budge her. Finally he yelled for help, and Mary Jane came running.

By now Snooty had become tired of this game, and once more she lay down, grunting. The children leaned back, yanking harder than ever. Suddenly the rope broke and Mary Jane and Willie went backwards, plop, into the mud.

Mary Jane scrambled to her feet, but Willie lay there, laughing. "You see," he said. "Even Snooty won't come to your party."

"Then I'll bring the party to her!" said Mary Jane, giggling. She ran back to the yard and

picked up her little acorn cake. Then she came
back to the pigsty and knelt in front of the sow.
Snooty's pink snout sniffed, her mouth opened,
and the cake disappeared.

Mary Jane stood up. "Come on, Willie. We'd better get washed before Mama comes."

On the back porch there was a big wooden tub where the members of the family washed their faces and hands before eating. Mrs. McLeod, who kept a neat house, insisted on clean hands and faces at mealtime. The two children took pails and ran to the stream that flowed past their yard. They dipped up pails of clear, cold water and made several trips to fill the tub. Then they carefully washed the mud from their faces and hands and legs.

"Our backs are muddy, too," Willie groaned. "Mama certainly will punish us."

Mary Jane was seldom at a loss for ideas. All at once she turned around and sat down in the water. Then she jounced up and down a few times and stood up, dripping.

"Am I clean?" she asked.

Willie was laughing. "Just about," he answered. A few minutes later he sat in the tub and bounced up and down. "Yes!" he screeched. "This is the way to get clean."

The two children had completely forgotten the work and their parents. Suddenly Mary Jane saw the members of the family coming back from the cotton patch. Her father led the little procession, his chopping hoe over his shoulder. Although he had worked hard all day in the field, his shoulders were square and his head erect. Patsy, Mary Jane's mother, followed. Like her husband, she was erect and stately.

Then came the brothers and sisters, from Sis Liz, the oldest girl still at home, to little Dolly, just younger than Mary Jane. Some of the older children had already left home. Sally and Sammie were both married and living in Sumter, fifteen miles away. The others were living away, working for white folks, but they came home whenever they could.

Patsy McLeod stared at the dripping children. "What have you been up to?"

"We fell in the mud and were just trying to wash up," Mary Jane explained.

Her mother shook her head, but she was too tired to scold. "Get in the house and take off those wet clothes," she ordered.

Fifteen minutes later, Mary Jane, wrapped in her grandmother's gray shawl, stood warming herself by the stove. Willie, snug in a piece of blanket, came to stand with her. Their mother was stirring a kettle of hominy grits and fatback for their supper.

Willie sniffed the good odor coming from cooking food. "Hominy grits are better than any old birthday cake," he said.

Mary Jane giggled. "At least they are better than mine, but anyhow I had a birthday. Now I'm nine years old, the same as Louise."

Danger in the Cotton Patch

MARY JANE awoke the next morning with the feeling that she had overslept. She sat up and rubbed her eyes, peering through the dimness of the room. Sure enough, everyone was gone except the two sisters who slept with her.

She jumped from the prickly straw mattress and slipped on her little calico dress. Then, barefooted, she ran into the kitchen.

Her mother was at the big square stove, stiring the mush of cowpeas and side-bacon. The older boys and girls were already eating hungrily. Mary Jane dashed out to the back porch where Willie was washing his hands. He held

a big flat bar of yellow homemade soap, trying to get a lather in the cold water.

"Yes, yes, sleepyhead!" he cried. "You're
about last as usual!"

"I'll be ready as soon as you are!" Mary Jane
answered. She splashed the water over her face.
"I guess I know enough to get out to the patch
as soon as it's day."

"You still have all your morning chores to do,"
Willie reminded her.

"So have you, I reckon."

Mary Jane was annoyed at herself for letting
her brother get ahead of her. Now she must
hurry. There were so many things to do before
she could eat breakfast.

She gave her face what her mother called "a
lick and a promise." Then she ran into the tiny
bedroom, plumped the straw mattress on her
bed, and smoothed the gray cotton coverlet.
Now she must take Old Star, the cow, out to pas-

ture. She felt triumphant when she saw that Willie was still busy feeding Old Bush. Maybe she could beat him in to breakfast.

She fastened the pasture gate and turned to see Willie racing for the house. With a toss of her head she dashed after him, churning the dusty path with her bare feet. Finally they reached the back door together.

Two or three stools had been pushed back from the table. Mary Jane and Willie sat down and began to eat from the bowls of steaming porridge their mother placed in front of them. Sis Liz was already washing empty bowls in a tin pan set on the back of the stove. Patsy McLeod insisted on having the cabin neat and clean before the family left for the field.

By the time this was done, all of them were ready for the day's work in the cotton patch, but first they must have morning prayer. It was unthinkable to go to the field without asking the Lord to watch over them during the day. They knelt on the clean dirt floor, swept until it gleamed like the polished wood floors in the big houses of the white folks. With arms folded and heads bent, they murmured "Hallelujah!" and "Amen!" as their father prayed.

"Dear Lord," Mr. McLeod began, "we thank Thee for all Thy blessings. Keep watch over us today. Bless our fields, that they will prosper. Hold us in Thine hands. Let us be safe in Thine everlasting arms!"

As the family started to the cotton patch, Mary Jane said, "I'll bet I finish my rows first."

"I don't care if you do!" Willie answered. "I don't know why you're so crazy about doing everything first and best. I'd just as soon be last and worst."

Mary Jane stared at him. "You never will amount to anything, Willie McLeod, but I intend to be somebody someday!"

"I just intend to be Willie McLeod." Willie danced a little jig in the gray light of dawn, whirling around his sister.

Mary Jane raised her face toward the sky. She drew in deep breaths of the crisp, cool morning air. As she looked toward the east, she noted streaks of light cutting the grayness of dawn. "The sun is coming up, Willie," she said.

"Sure it is. It does every morning."

"Do you think it comes up quicker over yonder? If we went out past the woods, would we see it before folks out here do?"

"Of course not! The sun rises the same time everywhere in the whole world."

"I wonder if it does," said Mary Jane.

"Yes, you wonder about too much. It makes no difference anyhow. We won't ever be out there beyond the woods to know."

Mary Jane's face was raised toward the sky. "I like to see the sun come up. It makes me feel like singing." She began one of the hymns she often heard in church and the others, walking ahead of her, joined in.

"I'll fall down on my knees
And face the rising sun.
O, Lord! have mercy if you please!"

Soon they came to the cotton patch, now gay with large white and purple blossoms. The McLeods always paused at the edge of the patch, staring at it with love. How lucky they were to own their land, their cabin, and their animals. Many Negro families had nothing.

Even many white families didn't own the land they lived on. They just dwelt in cabins on land owned by white people and worked, not for themselves but for the landowners. All they got for their work was barely enough of the crops they raised for them to live on.

The blossoming cotton plants were now as tall as Mary Jane. She stood between two rows of the green stalks and thought, "Here I am, Mary Jane McLeod. I am nine years old and I have a birthday, just like any other girl. I wonder if anyone will ever know that I'm standing here, in this green church, under the blue sky! Dear Lord, please let them know."

She began to chop vigorously at the weeds that seemed to pop up overnight. It had been a summer-long job, this weeding, but now there would be less to do. In two days the blossoms would wilt and drop off the stems, and the little green bolls would appear. Then, while the bolls grew round and fat with cotton, there would not be so much weeding.

Everything was cool and damp with dew. Mary Jane enjoyed the feeling of dampness on her bare feet, but after the sun came up, the ground became very hot. Beads of sweat formed on her forehead and ran down her face. It was going to be another hot day. Chopping weeds was hard work for anyone, but Mary Jane worked with energy. Engrossed in her own thoughts, she did not mind the work or the heat.

Suddenly she held her hoe in midair and stared at the ground with her dark eyes. "Here's a snake," she screeched.

Willie leaped between the rows, his hoe upraised. Both brothers and sisters came running, with the older brothers pushing ahead of their sisters. "A snake! A snake!" There was more excitement than alarm in their voices.

The hoes that had been chopping green weeds now began to chop at the slithering green snake, bright against the red sand of the furrow. The boys suddenly became ferocious hunters.

Mary Jane stood back, watching. She felt sick and sorrowful and ashamed. "Lord have mercy," she prayed.

Willie turned toward her. "It's dead! You needn't be scared any more."

"I'm not scared," Mary Jane whispered.

"Well, I saved you from that danger!"

Mary Jane stared at the mutilated snake lying on the ground. Had it really been a danger? She had been startled when she first saw the snake, but should she have been afraid?

With her hoe she scraped out a small pit and carefully nudged the broken body into its grave. She thought of the funerals she had attended and the mournful hymns people had sung. One came to her mind, and kneeling there alone in her "green church" she sang softly,

"Swing low, sweet chariot!
Coming for to carry me home!"

Singing softly, she returned to her weeding. From that day on, however, she kept a watch out for snakes. She would never again be startled into yelling, "Here's a snake!"

Mary Jane watched the bolls swell, knowing

that inside, somehow, mysteriously, the soft, white cotton was growing, pushing against its green cage. She wished she dared break one open to discover just what was happening. She wished she knew what made the cotton grow.

One night, after supper, while the children were waiting for evening hymn and prayer, Willie thought about Mary Jane and how she had not joined in killing the snake that July morning. He began to tease her. "Yes, Janie's afraid of a little snake."

His father frowned at him. "Hush, Willie! Janie's not afraid of a snake. She just knows a hoe is meant for chopping weeds, not for chopping garter snakes. She tends to her work. You could follow her example. Your rows aren't ever as clean as hers."

Mr. McLeod seldom gave such direct praise, and a feeling of pride swelled up in Mary Jane. It must have shown on her face, for Grandma

Sophie gave a dry laugh. "Don't let your father's words make you full of pride," she warned. "The Lord doesn't admire proud children."

Mary Jane bent her head to hide her face. She knew the reproof was merited, but her father had been right. She always did good work. Her rows were the cleanest of all in the patch.

"I can't help it because I work harder and faster than some of the others," she thought. "Somehow I just want to get things done and done right!" Then she remembered what her grandmother had said about proud children. "Dear Lord," she whispered, "please take some of the pride out of me."

Her father had begun to sing a familiar hymn and she joined in.

"When I went down to the field to pray,
　　Oh, rock of my soul!
My soul was happy and I stayed all day,
　　Oh, rock of my soul!"

34

Why Can't
I Read?

"Janie," her mother said one morning, "you won't have to go to the cotton patch today. I'll take you with me when I carry the ironing back to Mrs. McIntosh. You can carry the baby's bonnets, which have to be carried very carefully, so they won't be wrinkled."

Mary Jane's eyes lit up. "I'd love to carry them, and I'll be careful. Maybe the McIntoshes will be having another party."

"May I go, too, Mama?" Willie begged.

"You have work to do this forenoon, so you must stay here and do it." Willie sulked, but he knew there was no use to argue.

Patsy handed Mary Jane the baby bonnets she had washed and ironed so carefully. "My, but they're pretty!" Mary Jane said. She held them up, admiring the ruffles of lace and embroidery and the pink and blue ribbons. Her mother picked up the basket that held the other ironed clothes, swung it up on her head, and set out, with Mary Jane beside her.

Mary Jane found it difficult to keep up with her mother. She dropped behind a little, and as she followed her mother, she watched how she walked, so straight and prideful.

They came to the big white house where the McIntoshes lived. The McIntoshes weren't as rich now as they had been before the war that freed the slaves, but they still owned a great plantation and could hire folks to do heavy work around the house and grounds. The fields had been let out to sharecroppers, both black and white, who lived in tiny cabins nearby.

As Mary Jane and her mother started around the house to the back door, the little girl gazed at the glass window spread like a fan above the gleaming white door. The brass knocker sparkled in the sunlight.

She wished that she could see what lay behind that door, but she probably never would. Her mother took the baby bonnets from her. "You wait out here, Janie," she said, and went up the steps to the back door.

Mary Jane looked around for something to do. Off to one side was a small house, painted white like the big house, with a brass knocker on the front door and with tiny glass windows. Mary Jane knew it was a playhouse for the two McIntosh girls, Louise and Henrietta.

She had seen it before and had wondered what it was like inside. Did it have small furniture? Did it have a back door? Did it have more than one room? No one was watching, so Mary

Jane tiptoed around to the back and there, sure enough, was a back door. It was standing open, and she couldn't help peeking inside.

Louise and Henrietta were there playing with their dolls. Louise looked up and saw the visitor. "Hello, Janie," she said. Then, imitating her mother's voice, she continued, "Did you come to get the wash?"

Mary Jane giggled. She had played make-believe by herself often enough to be able to enter into the game. "Yes, Miss Louise." She tried to sound like her mother.

The two little girls came toward Mary Jane. Louise was carrying a beautiful doll. "I'm sorry," she said in her make-believe grown-up voice, "but I just haven't had time to get it ready. If you'll just take care of the baby for a minute, I'll see what I can do."

She handed Mary Jane the doll and flounced out of the little house. Mary Jane held the doll carefully, her heart thumping at having such a lovely thing in her hands. She touched one of the golden curls that fell to the doll's shoulders. It was soft as new cotton.

Henrietta kept on playing and gave little attention to their visitor. Mary Jane wanted to see everything. She looked past the doll's head at the small table and chairs. There was even a tiny rocking chair for the doll! On the table were several books. One was gay with color, and seemed especially attractive.

On the cover was a bright picture of a golden-haired little girl and a brown-haired boy. They were playing with a dog and laughing. Mary Jane had never before seen anything like this, except on the calendar at the crossroads store.

There was a book at home, a Bible, but it was nothing like this. She placed the doll carefully in its chair and picked up the book. She opened it and stared at row after row of little black marks. What did these marks mean? What were they saying?

She did not hear Louise come back and was startled when the little girl said, "I asked you

to mind the baby! Why are you looking at a book when you can't read?"

Mary Jane laid the book on the table. Then she turned and ran from the room, out into the sunlight. Tears stung her eyelids. She wanted to scream. She flung herself down on the grass beside the gravel walk and dug her fists into her eyes. Why couldn't she read? Why? Why? Then, used to speaking aloud, she looked up at the sky and prayed.

"Lord, dear Lord, why can't I read? Please, please show me how! Please let me have a book of my own! Show me how to read!"

When her mother came out of the big house, Mary Jane ran to her. "Why can't I read, Mama? Why can't I read?"

"It's not an easy thing to learn, Janie. You have to go to school."

"I'll go, Mama. I'll go."

"Only white children go to school, Janie," her

mother explained. "There aren't any schools for children like you."

"Why not, Mama? Why not? Why aren't there schools for children like me?"

"What has happened, Janie?" her mother asked. "What has happened to you?"

Mary Jane managed to get control of her feelings. She told her mother about the book—the beautiful book with colored pictures—and how she wanted to know what the black marks said. "I held it in my hands, Mama. I saw the marks. I know they told a story, but I couldn't tell what it was. I can't read."

"Don't cry, child. I've seen books like that sometimes in white folks' houses, but I never looked close at one. A person needs only one book—the Good Book. We have that."

"But we can't read it!"

"We know what it says. The preacher tells us that. I reckon it would be a fine thing if we could just open up the book ourselves and read what it says, but that's not for us."

"Why? You and Grandma say we're free. Then why aren't we free to read?"

"You're a strange one, Janie," her mother said. "You have ideas other children never have. Well, just hold onto them. Then, maybe, for you, some of them will come true."

Mary Jane said nothing, but her heart was beating out a little song. "For you, for you, reading may come true. Dear Lord, please let it come true. Let me learn how to read!"

Fear in the Night

MARY JANE was helping her grandmother sort and clean collard greens for supper. They sat out in the yard, under the shade of the great oak tree with its dangling Spanish moss.

"These hot days are best of the whole year!" the old woman said with a contented sigh. "That good sun warms my bones like no fire can."

"I like these hot days, too," Mary Jane agreed. "While the bolls are getting fat, we don't have much work to do in the cotton patch. Now we have more time for doing other interesting things. I like all-day singings and I like camp meetings and I like moonlight parties."

"When you work, you're the hardest working child I ever saw, but you enjoy doing other things, too," Grandmother declared.

"I wish there would be a camp meeting to-night," Mary Jane began, but her grandmother's laugh interrupted her.

"There is going to be one, Janie. Hasn't your father told you about it?"

"Where, Grandma? Where will it be?"

"It will be right here, child, in this very yard," Grandmother said. "Preacher Ellison will be here, and your father told all the folks around to come hear him preach tonight."

Willie had come up with another bucket of greens he'd collected down by the stream. He frowned as he put the greens down. "Yes, and it'll probably rain and spoil our fun."

"This isn't a fun meeting. It's going to be a preaching affair."

"I like this kind of meeting best," said Mary

Jane. "I like the preaching and the praying and the singing and the hallelujahs, too."

"There'll be plenty of that, I reckon," the old woman said. "Preacher Ellison is going to be here for supper, so we'll need more of these collards. He is a great one for eating collards and fatback."

Willie went off to gather more greens. Mary Jane stared at the sky. "The Lord won't let it rain, will he, Grandma?"

"He'll do what he thinks best, child," her grandmother answered. "It's not for us to dictate what will be and what won't be."

Preacher Ellison arrived just before suppertime. He was given the honor of saying "Thank You" to the Lord for the good food that was on the table. He had a deep, rich voice. Mary Jane felt little chills run up and down her spine as she listened to the big words that rolled so easily off the preacher's tongue.

She had a powerful voice, too. "But not like his!" she told herself, and silently pushed her own voice down low in her throat, trying to make it richer.

Willie's bare toes kicked her under the table. Evidently he wanted her to watch the preacher, who was piling small mountains of greens onto his knife and transferring them expertly to his mouth. Both children could tell as they watched the preacher that Grandma was right. He certainly liked greens.

After supper, while the older girls cleared the table, Mary Jane went through the four rooms of the cabin, collecting the candles. It was her evening chore to trim the wicks and scrape away the melted wax from the holders.

When she finished working on the candles, she took the one glass lamp from a shelf. This lamp had been given to her mother on her wedding day. The Wilsons, who had owned Patsy, had been kind and generous to her and Sam and had given them a real wedding.

The lamp never was used unless there was company, because it burned coal oil, and the Negroes were charged as much as three and four times what white folks were charged for such things as coal oil and candles and sugar. They had to buy those things because they couldn't raise them or get along without them.

Mary Jane trimmed the lampwick and carefully washed the glass chimney. Now the lamp was ready to be used if her father and the preacher wanted to talk after the meeting.

Tonight Mary Jane had a special job, since meeting would be held in the yard. She must make smoke sticks to keep away the mosquitoes that swarmed in from the swamp nearby. She hated the mosquitoes and would gladly have wished the swamp dried up, but it was such a good place for raising rice. She loved rice. A bowl of hot rice with cowpeas and fatback was about the best supper she could think of.

She went out back to get some straight, stout willow branches which her older brothers had gathered. She wrapped a few rags around one end of each branch and tied them firmly in place. Then she dipped them into a can of crude black oil. She lighted each one at the firebox of the stove and carried it outside to hand it to one of the guests already arriving.

Mary Jane's older brothers and sisters came and found places to sit, on the steps or the ground, which had been swept clean. Her mother came, too, carrying Hattie. Willie brought out his grandmother's rocking chair and Mary Jane helped the old woman to her place.

"Let us pray!" The preacher's rich voice rolled through the smoky darkness.

"Willie was wrong!" Mary Jane whispered to her grandmother. "It didn't rain!"

49

"Hush, child! Pray!"

Mary Jane looked up at the sky. The big bright stars seemed almost to touch the treetops. All around there were soft chirps of katydids and crickets. From far off in the woods came an occasional baying of dogs hot on the trail of a raccoon or an opossum. Mary Jane felt a deep sense of happiness. She began to pray silently, along with the preacher.

In his prayer the preacher mentioned all the things the Negroes wanted and needed. Every little while the worshipers would murmur "Amen" or sing out "Hallelujah!" Mary Jane hugged her knees and sang out with the others.

Then came the singing. Mary Jane's rich voice rang out. She knew the words to every hymn that was sung at church on Sundays. She didn't have to mumble and stutter as some of the other children did. The preacher smiled at her to show that he appreciated her singing.

50

After the singing came the sermon, and Preacher Ellison was noted for his sermons. He stood up in front and urged all the people in the audience not to sin lest they suffer fire and brimstone after they died.

Mary Jane shivered. It was scary in the darkness, lit only by wavering, smoky torches, to hear about fire and brimstone waiting for sinners. She looked across at Willie. He was scared, too. Then the people began to sing again.

"Carried away! Carried away!
I am carried away to Jesus!"

Suddenly Mary Jane was aware of another sound—one not connected with the singing, the worshiping people, or the lovely summer evening. It was the sound of many horses' hoofs pounding the soft dust of the road.

Other people had heard it, too. They lifted their heads and turned their eyes toward the

51

road that ran from Mayesville, five miles away, past the McLeod cabin.

Preacher Ellison stopped in the middle of a fiery warning. "Let us sing!" he said in his rich, strong voice. It didn't tremble, even a little bit.

"Nobody knows the trouble I've seen,
Nobody knows but Jesus."

All the people stood up, drawing a little closer together, and their voices rang out. Mary Jane was still scared, but she was angry, too. The hymn came from her throat, not only loud and clear, but with a defiant note. She knew very well who was coming!

Willie's mouth was open, but he did not sing with the others. Little drops of sweat formed on his forehead and chin, and he had good reason to be scared. He had been in Mayesville the night Lemuel Jackson's cabin had been burned to the ground by these night riders.

Everyone was pretending to be looking only at Preacher Ellison, but Mary Jane knew that everyone was watching the road, just as she was. Then the night riders came into sight, out to scare Negroes and even to harm them for little or no reason.

Mary Jane kept on singing, but she became even more angry. "These men have glass in their windows, but we have only wooden shutters! Why do they ride around to scare and hurt us?"

The procession slowed a little as it passed the group of worshipers, but it did not stop. On down the road it went, the horses' hoofs thudding on the soft dirt. When the last ghostly rider was out of sight, the singing came to an end, and a chorus of fervent "Hallelujahs" was breathed softly by everyone.

But the scare had put a damper on the services, and the people soon began to leave. They shook the preacher's hand, said good night to

54

the McLeods, and quietly drifted away. There was no conversation or laughter.

Patsy McLeod and all the McLeod children went soberly to bed. Her husband lighted the pretty glass lamp and set it on the table. Then he and Preacher Ellison drew up chairs and sat close together, talking in low earnest voices. The two of them often talked together in this manner after a meeting, but tonight they had more than usual to talk about. They were alarmed by the rising terror manifested by the night riders in their part of the country.

A Promise
Is Made

WHILE HER FATHER and the preacher talked, Mary Jane lay awake, thinking. There was a great deal to think about, such as night riders going around to scare colored folks. Her father had explained everything the first time white-robed riders had passed by their cabin. She had been dreadfully scared that time.

"Just keep away from them," her father had said, "and don't be afraid of them. They're just some white men out for a lark."

"But it's not Halloween!" Willie had protested. "Why are men riding around dressed in white robes when it isn't Halloween?"

56

Sam McLeod had shaken his head sadly. "I reckon nobody can explain why they want to frighten us. Just don't bother them and hope that they don't bother us."

Remembering this, Mary Jane shivered a little, there in the small, hot bedroom. Then she thought about her family and how lucky they were to own their own land and cabin and cow and mule. Not many families had so much.

At the same time she thought about how hard all the members of the family worked. Her father and older brothers worked hard in the field and had even built the small cabin where the family lived. Her mother not only worked in the field during the day, but she spent the evening cooking, washing, and ironing.

At this particular time of the year Mary Jane and the other small children had less work to do than usual. They always had things to do in the yard and the cabin, but during the long, hot afternoons they could play, or fish, or go out hunting fruit. Wild berries grew in the thickets along the stream, and peaches and apples ripened in nearby orchards. Once these orchards had been carefully tended, but since the war they had been abandoned because there were no slaves to do the work.

Mary Jane and Willie and Dolly often sat in the shade of the trees and munched some of the sun-ripe fruit which they had gathered. Dolly, almost three summers younger than Mary Jane, would lick the juice from her dripping lips. She was quieter than her sister, but she tried to do everything the older girl did. Unlike Willie, she had not given up hope of beating her sister at work or at games.

Every day, no matter what she had to do, Mary Jane took time to run out to the cotton patch to see if a boll had burst open. She knew it was too soon, though she didn't realize that it took six weeks from the time the blossom wilted and fell for the cotton to ripen.

One hot afternoon in August, her patience was rewarded. A green pod had burst into a five-pointed star, against which clung a puff of soft, white cotton. She raced back to the cabin. "The cotton's out! The cotton's out!"

By the next morning the whole field was a sea of white. The dark green of yesterday was lost under the puffs of snowy cotton. Everyone, even including baby Hattie, would go to the field to-day. It was like a holiday. Cotton picking was work, but it was fun, too.

The McLeods were up long before the summer sky was streaked with light. They hastily ate breakfast and did the morning chores. However, they listened to a longer prayer than usual. Sam McLeod was thankful for a good cotton crop that had been preserved from weevils, bugs, storm, fire, and other disasters.

The whole family left the cabin at the same time. Everyone, even Old Sophie, was happy at the thought of the day in the sun, gathering the stuff that meant the only cash money they would have all year. Each carried a long croker sack slung over the shoulder. Its gaping mouth hung just at the right place for hands to reach. There must be no wasted motion.

There was a tingle of frost in the morning air. The grass was wet with dew. Mary Jane wriggled her toes in the cool dampness. Her croker sack was so long it dragged on the ground behind her. She was such a quick and steady worker that she needed the same size sack the grown-ups used. Dolly, who had very little experience in picking cotton, had a smaller sack strung across her narrow shoulder.

"Do you expect to fill that croker sack?" Mary Jane asked her sister.

"I certainly do!" Dolly replied. "I wanted a

60

big sack like yours, but Mama wouldn't give me one. I know I could fill a big one."

"How many pounds do you plan to pick today, Mary Jane?" Willie asked, running to catch up with his sisters.

"Two hundred pounds," replied Mary Jane.

"You can't pick that much! Why, Papa doesn't pick much more than that! You must think you're some sort of champion!"

"Yes, I plan to be the champion of the McLeods today," Mary Jane retorted.

Sam McLeod carefully apportioned the patch, assigning certain rows to each child. "Pick the plants clean!" he warned. "There's no use leaving money hanging on the plants."

Mary Jane went to her place. Walking down between two rows of plants, she swiftly began to pull off the white puffs. She used both hands at once, and kept picking and stuffing the cotton into the gaping sack.

It required a certain deft twist to remove the cotton puff quickly and cleanly from its green jacket, but Mary Jane had learned exactly how to do this. She liked to look back and not see a single gob of white behind her. Even the ground between her rows was cleaner than most. Willie fumbled a good deal, and wisps of white dotted the red sand where he worked.

As the sun came up, Mary Jane's mother began to sing, and the others joined in.

> "Ezekiel saw the wheel,
>   Away up in the middle of the air.
>   Ezekiel saw the wheel,
>   Away up in the middle of the air.
>   The big wheel runs by faith,
>   The little wheel runs by the grace of God.
>   Ezekiel saw the wheel,
>   Away up in the middle of the air."

Bit by bit, Mary Jane's sack grew heavier and heavier. Her shoulder began to ache with the weight of the sack. As the sun beat down hotter and hotter, sweat dripped from under the red bandanna that she wore around her head for protection. Later in the forenoon she began to be hungry. She looked at the sky and saw that the sun was almost overhead.

Her mother was nowhere to be seen. She had taken Hattie and Old Sophie back to the cabin. In a little while, her father would start for the cabin. Then the others could traipse after him and, when they got there, their midday meal would be ready. Then all would wash up outside the cabin and go in to eat.

By now all the children were casting anxious glances at their father. Picking cotton was fun, but it made folks very hungry. So when Sam McLeod hoisted his half-filled sack onto his back, every one of the McLeod children did the same thing. They were right at their father's heels when he left the field.

Mary Jane and Willie and Dolly had to wait while the older children washed up. "Being oldest is almost like being white folks," Willie grumbled. "You get to do everything first. You wash first, you eat first, you get first seats when you go to church."

"You don't go to bed first," his sister reminded him. "That's what we have to do."

"Yes, that's one thing I'd let them do first, if I could," Willie said.

Patsy had prepared an extra good dinner to celebrate the first day of cotton picking. There was a large kettle of rice and cowpeas cooked with big chunks of fatback. There also were hunks of corn pone with a pitcher of sorghum to pour on. Both parents and children ate heartily to satisfy their ravenous appetites. Afterward, while the sun was still high, they would take a few minutes to rest.

The younger children were the last to finish

scraping their bowls. The older ones finished first and went outside to sprawl in the shade of the oak. Now and then someone spoke drowsily, but there was no animated conversation.

Mary Jane gave one last swipe of corn pone to sop up the trace of sorghum in the bottom of her bowl. She stopped, with the sweet morsel half-way to her lips. She listened carefully to a strange conversation taking place outside. Her father was saying, "Good day, ma'am. Are you looking for someone?"

In answer came a voice Mary Jane had never heard before. It was a Negro woman's voice, but softer and with a different sound from the voices of the neighborhood. It said, "Mr. McLeod, I am Miss Emma Wilson."

Mary Jane stuffed the corn pone in her mouth and went to stand in the open door. Something strange was going on. No one ever called her father Mr. McLeod! Outside was a young Negro woman. She wore a black straw hat with white daisies on it. Mary Jane listened.

The young lady went on, "Mr. McLeod, I am going around the neighborhood to let the colored people know that there is going to be a school for their children at Mayesville."

Mrs. McLeod joined Mary Jane in the doorway. The little girl took hold of her mother's arm, as if she needed to be kept from falling.

"There's going to be a school for colored children?" Sam McLeod asked, unbelieving.

"Yes, that's right. The Missions for Freedmen of the Trinity Presbyterian Church up North has decided to open a school at Mayesville. I'll be the teacher of the school, and anyone may attend. Of course it will be difficult for some families to spare children. There's always so much work to be done, but I hope to get at least one child from every family."

She came toward Patsy. "Mrs. McLeod, do

66

you understand about the school? Can I count on you to send a child or two?"

"I don't know," Patsy began. "We always have so much work to do. We own this place, you see, and have to do everything to keep it up." She spoke with evident pride.

"That's wonderful! I am sure a child from such a family would be the very sort that could benefit from school." Miss Wilson looked at Mary Jane. "What about this child?"

"She learns fast and has a hankering after knowledge," Patsy said.

Mary Jane wanted to yell out, "Please let me go! Let me go to school!" But she just scuffed at the doorstep with her bare toe.

"Maybe this is not a good time," Miss Wilson went on, "but perhaps you can spare her during the winter, after the cotton is picked."

Mary Jane could stand it no longer. She tugged at her mother's arm. "Mama, you said maybe it would come true for me, and it has! Please let me go to school!"

Miss Wilson smiled at her eagerness. "You've thought about school, honey?"

"I want to learn how to read! I want to read more than anything else. If I go to school I'll learn how, won't I?"

"Yes, I promise that if you come to our school you'll learn to read and to write and to do numbers. I hope you'll learn many other things, but reading I can promise."

Her parents looked at each other. "Let her go, Patsy," Sam said. "We'll miss such a good worker, but she deserves the chance."

Patsy nodded. "Yes, Miss Wilson. As soon as the cotton is in, Janie can go to school."

Mary Jane waited to hear no more. She gave a leap down the step and went bounding through the yard, yelling, "Willie! Willie! I'm going to school! Mama's promised."

Miss Wilson smiled. "I only wish all my pupils would feel like that!" She told Sam and Patsy good-by and went on down the road to talk with other families.

Mary Jane didn't go back into the house. She grabbed her croker sack and set out for the cotton patch to continue her work. She would pick so much cotton, her parents would know that she was worth sending to school.

Willie followed her. "Are you crazy, Janie?" he asked. "Are you going to walk five or ten miles every day just to learn to read?"

"Yes, I am!" Then she began to sing a hymn that was just meant for today.

"Listen Brother! Listen Brother!
Don't pay no attention to Satan, Brother!
I heard from the Lord today!"

The Cotton
Is Sold

THAT EVENING while Mary Jane waited for her turn at supper, she walked over to the small table and looked down at the family Bible. This big book, which was the one book that the family owned, was seldom opened. It had been in the family for a number of years.

Just after the slaves had been set free, "Bible men" came through the land, selling large, beautiful Bibles. One of these Bibles cost ten dollars —more money than most of the Negro families made in a whole year.

A "Bible man" had come to the cabin to sell a Bible, and Old Sophie wanted one the worst

71

way. So Sam, usually wise and thrifty, had put his mark on a paper. After that, every month the man had come around for money, and Sam always managed to pay him some. Old Sophie always told this story with a chuckle. "Somehow we always had money for the man. The Lord helped us pay for His Book."

Tonight Mary Jane ran her pink palms over the dark brown cover. Then she opened the book. She bent low to study the black marks by the dim candlelight. Someday she would know what those marks meant.

She touched a fingertip to the words and then quickly drew it back. She felt guilty somehow, feeling words whose meaning she couldn't even guess. But she was going to school, and she was going to learn how to read.

This thought made the long, hot days in the cotton patch pass quickly. Mary Jane no longer watched the sun to know when the midday break would come. She picked feverishly, think-ing all the time that as soon as the cotton was in, she could go to school.

When the workers sang, her voice was the loudest of all, but in her mind there were always questions. What was school like? How would she learn to read? Would it be difficult?

"It won't be very hard!" she told Willie. "I just know it won't."

Each evening at dusk the McLeods left the cotton patch, dragging their heavy sacks. In the yard the sacks were emptied onto the ever-grow-ing pile. Little Dolly and baby Hattie loved to jump up and down in the fluffy white mass. On starlit nights, the older folks often sat outside for a bit of chatting and singing before going to bed. Then Mary Jane would scoop out a little nest in the cotton and lie there looking up at the stars and dreaming of school.

Fortunately, before any rain came, the cotton

was all picked and packed into stout bags to be taken to the cotton gin. Dolly asked, "Why does Papa take the cotton to the gin? What do the men at the gin do to it?"

"They take out the seeds, or the little lumps that you can feel inside each gob of cotton," Mary Jane explained. "Grandma says that a long time ago folks didn't have cotton patches. Then this machine came along, and now everybody has a cotton patch."

Sam McLeod fastened boards to the old wagon box so it would be deep enough to hold the sacks of cotton. Willie hitched up Old Bush and made ready to go with his father to the gin.

"Do you want to come along, Janie?" her father asked at the last minute.

Mary Jane's eyes lighted up. "I surely do, Papa. I've never been to the gin."

"Yes, yes, Tagalong, that's Janie McLeod," Willie teased.

"I want to know what happens to the cotton! Besides, why shouldn't I go?"

Their father interrupted the argument. "Hush, children, or you'll both stay home."

"He won't leave me!" Willie whispered. "He needs me to help with the cotton."

"He could take Luke!" Mary Jane whispered back. "He doesn't have to take you."

Willie sat on the rickety seat beside his father, and Mary Jane perched on the piled-up sacks. "Goodness me!" she chuckled. "I'm going to the cotton gin!" She had a feeling that something special was going to happen.

Clem Hastings, the foreman at the cotton gin, welcomed Sam McLeod with a hearty greeting. Mary Jane climbed down from her perch and wandered about, staring at everything.

Her father and brother unloaded the heavy sacks and carried them, one by one, to a wooden platform in front of the building. Beside the platform a strange contraption with a long black arm attracted her attention. There was a chunk of brass that slid along the arm, and a chain with a hook at one end dangled from the bar.

Willie and his father hoisted up a sack of cotton and hung it on the hook. Then Clem Hastings slid the chunk of brass along, till the iron arm slowly moved.

"What's he doing?" Mary Jane asked.

"He's weighing the cotton."

"Why is he weighing it?"

"So he'll know how much to pay Papa."

"What does he do with the cotton?"

"Well, inside that building there's a machine that takes out all the seeds. Then the cotton is tied up in bundles called bales and sent down to Charleston. There it is put on a ship and sent up North somewhere."

Mary Jane looked at her brother with new respect. "My, but you're smart, Willie!"

Sack after sack was brought over and weighed. Each time Clem looked closely at the black iron arm and made marks in a little book. At last all the sacks were weighed, and Clem grinned at Sam. "You evidently had a mighty good crop this year," he said. He tore the sheet out of his book and handed it to Sam. "Take this to the office and get your money."

"How much did it come to?" Sam asked.

Clem shrugged impatiently. "It's all written down there. Just take it into the office and the clerk will pay you."

"But how many pounds did I have?" Sam persisted quietly.

Clem frowned. Someone else was waiting to weigh in his cotton. "I told you, Sam! It's all down on that paper."

Mary Jane felt a shout rising in her throat. She wanted to yell. "How much was it? Tell my father how much it was!"

By now Sam had taken her arm and was gently propelling her toward the door of the long wooden building. "Why didn't you make him tell you, Papa?" Mary Jane asked.

Sam shrugged his shoulders. "He just knew we couldn't read or figure."

Mary Jane stared at the paper. The black marks meant nothing to her, and she knew they meant nothing to her father. What if Clem had made a mistake? What if he had cheated them? If he had been honest, wouldn't he have answered her father? Wait till she learned to read! Things would be different, then.

Willie stayed with the wagon while Mary Jane and her father went into the office. In the dim, dusty room, a man took Sam's slip of paper. He looked at it, frowned, and opened a small drawer. Then he counted out round silver dollars. "You did pretty well this year," he said. "What will you do with all this cash?"

"He's going to send me to school!" Mary Jane just had to tell someone outside the family.

The clerk looked over the rim of his glasses. "You don't say! They're sending Negroes to school now! What's the world coming to?"

Mary Jane felt as she always did when someone said something ugly. She was angry and shamed and hurt, all at the same time. She turned and walked out of the office, her head high.

Her father followed her. He patted Mary Jane's head. "Don't let things bother you, Janie. The only way for us to get along is to ignore things that hurt us." He lifted her up into the wagon. Then he said cheerfully, "I'll tell you what let's do! We'll go on to Mayesville and spend some of this cash. I have some bills to pay and I might as well pay them today."

Mary Jane's spirits rose. "My goodness," she said happily. "We're going to Mayesville. I surely do love to go to town."

Willie looked up at his father. "Are you go-ing to buy us a piece of candy?"

"Just wait and see, boy! Just wait!"

Mary Jane began to sing loudly and clearly, and her father and brother joined in. She didn't know why, but she had chosen a song the Ne-groes sang when they were slaves. It was one of her father's favorites.

> "Didn't the Lord deliver Daniel,
> Didn't the Lord deliver Daniel,
> Didn't the Lord deliver Daniel
> Out of the lion's den."

"Papa," said Mary Jane, interrupting her sing-ing long enough to ask a question. "The Lord delivered you from slavery, didn't he?"

"He certainly did, child!"

"Now He's going to deliver me from the way I am, not able to read. I wasn't able to know how much cotton we took to the gin. Oh, I just can't wait to be delivered."

A Gift for Janie

WHEN THEY REACHED Mayesville the two children waited in the wagon while their father went into one building after another. Each time he came out grinning.

"The mortgage is paid," he said one time. Then, "The cotton seed is paid for!" and another time, "Old Bush's oats are paid for."

Mary Jane giggled. "It's lucky that folks let us pay up after the cotton is sold! We might have to go hungry if they didn't."

"No, we wouldn't," Willie told her. "I'd go fishing and catch so many perch that we couldn't eat all of them at once. I'd go hunting and shoot so many raccoons and opossums that we would really stuff ourselves."

"Where would you get your money for shotgun shells?" asked his sister.

"I'd get some white folks to give me shells for half what I caught," Willie said. "They would do that, some of them."

Sam McLeod came out of a building and climbed up beside Willie. "Now for the store!"

They drove down past the houses and cabins to the crossroads, where the store was located in a small wooden building, two stories high. The merchandise was on the first floor. Gomer Cowley, the owner, and his family lived above the store. He was a friendly man, and the Negroes liked to trade with him.

Sam tied Old Bush to a rail in front of the store. Mary Jane and Willie hopped down and followed him inside. The two children thought the store was a wonderful place.

They gazed about them. In the middle of the room was a big fat-bellied stove, set in a box of sand so the heat from the fire wouldn't burn the floor. Chairs and upended boxes stood in a circle around the stove. Sometimes white men, loafing and gossiping and telling tall stories, occupied all these seats, but today there was no one else in the store.

The store was full of enchanting things. The walls, from floor to ceiling, were lined with shelves on which lay bolts of bright calico and gingham. Boxes and bottles and tin cans were stacked so high you couldn't count them.

Mary Jane's nose twitched as she smelled the strange, lovely odor of the store. There were large open barrels of soda crackers and cowpeas, dried beans, sugar, dried apples and sweet potatoes. There were jugs of sorghum and great yellow cakes of cheese. In addition to the odor of all these foods, there was a sharp, tingling smell of coal oil or kerosine that had leaked out of a big tin container.

Best of all were the glass candy jars filled with peppermint sticks, horehound bars, licorice whips, and lemon drops. These jars were placed on the counter, next to the baskets of eggs and the big cake of cheese.

"Looking at these jars of candy makes my mouth water," Mary Jane said. "Just seeing them makes me sort of taste them."

Willie nodded. "I like peppermint sticks most of all, but I never have had enough, even when I had a whole stick to myself. Yes, once I really had a whole stick to myself."

"What is it today, Sam?" the storekeeper asked. "Did you have a good crop? Most folks around here aren't complaining this year."

"Yes, I had a pretty good crop," Sam McLeod answered. "Now I have enough money from the crop to buy a few things we need."

While Mary Jane and Willie feasted their eyes and noses on the bright, fragrant candies, their father picked out the things he wanted. He was a thrifty, sensible man, so he bought only the things the family needed.

At last he turned to the children. "Have you seen anything you'd like?" he asked. They didn't answer, but just looked at the candy.

"Give them each a peppermint stick," he said. The storekeeper opened a jar and took out two long, red and white striped sticks of candy. Willie grabbed one of the sticks and muttered, "Thank you," but Mary Jane hung back.

"What's the matter, child?" her father asked. "Have you lost your taste for candy?"

"No," Mary Jane said, "but I'd rather have something for school." She looked up at the storekeeper. "I'm going to school next week. I'm going to school here in Mayesville."

"You are going to school! Well, I heard that

86

some folks up North were going to start a school here for black children, but I didn't think they'd get any pupils."

"I'll be a pupil at the school, and I'm going to learn to read," said Mary Jane.

"Good," said the storekeeper.

Mr. McLeod looked around the store. "What do you have that she could use in school?"

"I want something to write with," Mary Jane said eagerly, "but I don't know what."

Mr. Cowley took something black, with a frame around it, from a shelf. The frame, which was about as large as the cover of the family Bible, was decorated with pretty red yarn.

"How about this?" he asked. Then, seeing that they didn't know what the object was, he went on, "It's for writing. See, here's a special pencil. I'll show you."

He took a thin little gray "stick" in his hand, made some movements, and white marks appeared on the black surface. The stick, or pencil as he'd called it, made a horrible scratching noise, but it sounded like music to Mary Jane. The pencil was talking to her in its own scratchy voice. She couldn't tell what it was saying, but she would learn. She turned toward her father, as if to beg for the slate.

"How much is it?" Sam asked slowly.

"It's not much more than a peppermint stick," the storekeeper said, "and it's something a child needs in school. You can rub off the writing and put some more on."

"I'll take it," said Sam, handing the slate to Mary Jane. "How much do I owe you?"

"Be careful of it, Janie. It'll break if you drop it." As if she ever would be so careless, Mary Jane thought.

Now the buying was finished. Sam and the children gathered up the bundles and went to the wagon. Willie was sucking on his pepper-

mint stick and Mary Jane was clutching her slate
to her chest. They climbed up to their places and
their father untied Old Bush, took his place on
the wagon seat, and lifted the reins.

Willie turned around to his sister. "Do you want a taste?" He held out his candy.

Mary Jane gave the sweet, tangy stick a few licks with her tongue and handed it back. "I'll write something for you on my slate as soon as I learn how," she promised. It was the only way she could think of to share her own precious gift with her brother.

At the edge of town, Old Bush's plodding steps brought them to a crowd of white boys and young men. As the McLeods came closer, one of these yelled, "Hey, Uncle, what did you buy at the store? Have you any money left?"

Another shouted, "Did you buy anything good to eat? What about sharing it?"

Mary Jane saw Willie's back stiffen as he hid his candy on the seat. Sam merely kept on driving and gave no sign that he had heard the boys shouting. He didn't urge Old Bush to go any faster, but just let him go on as before.

One of the boys picked up a stone and threw it at Old Bush. It struck the mule on the flank, and he lifted his head and snorted. The boys howled with laughter, but they didn't come any closer. They went on shouting to Sam and the children but didn't throw any more stones. In a few minutes the wagon passed on down the road and left them behind.

Willie's shoulders relaxed. "What would you do if they came after us?" he asked.

"I don't really know, child. I never pick cotton till the boll bursts, and I never figure what I'll do until I have to do it."

Mary Jane looked at her father. How wise he was, and how brave! He hadn't been at all scared. She squared her own shoulders. Her father was right. The way to get along with persons like that was to ignore their actions. Maybe, someday after she and all the other Negroes learned to read, things would be different.

Off to School

MARY JANE awakened on Monday morning filled with a strange mixture of feelings. She was scared and eager and happy all at the same time, but she was careful not to let anything but happiness show. No one must know that she was afraid. She put on her brand new dress of checked gingham and went out of the bedroom to stand in front of her grandmother.

"Will you button my dress, Grandma?" she asked. This was the very first dress she had ever had with real buttons and buttonholes down the back. All her dresses had just been straight sack-like affairs that slipped over her head.

92

"My goodness, Janie, you certainly look fine!" her grandmother exclaimed. "Turn around and let me get at those little buttons." Her old fingers fumbled at the unaccustomed task, but finally every button was fastened.

"Wash very carefully, Janie!" her mother warned from the stove where she was stirring the grits. "Then bring that bit of comb and let me fix your hair. No child of mine is going off to school with hair like a rat's nest."

Mary Jane had taken a good bath the night before, so she would be extra sweet and clean for this great adventure. Now she went out to the back porch to wash her face and hands.

Her older brothers and sisters stood back to let her have their places. This was the first sign of the extra importance she was to have in the family. She acknowledged it with a trembly grin. She scrubbed her face and hands and then took the broken comb to her mother.

This morning Patsy McLeod left the cooking to fifteen-year-old Sis Liz. She sat down on a stool and drew Mary Jane between her knees. Then she set to work combing the thick, curly hair that covered Mary Jane's head and hung down over her shoulders.

Very carefully she parted the hair in sections, from front to back and from left to right, into small, perfect squares. Then she braided the hair in each square into a tight little braid and tied it with a bit of red wool.

"There you are, Janie," her mother said, "and you surely look handsome."

Mary Jane went to look at herself in the small mirror that hung near the door. She didn't think she was pretty. Her grandmother had often said, "You're by no means a beauty, but you're smart, and that's more important."

Mary Jane was especially pleased with her appearance in the mirror. She liked her hair with its contrasting red bows, and her eyes, which were bright and sparkling.

"I don't care!" she thought. "I don't care how I look or what kind of clothes I have. All I want is to learn how to read. Nothing else is of much account to me."

She went to the table, but she was too excited to eat. She wanted to set out for school, even though it was still dark outside. She had never walked to Mayesville and did not know how long it would take. This was her first day and she was determined not to be late. She tried to eat her grits, but they stuck in her throat.

"You've got to eat something, Janie," her father told her gently. "It's a five-mile walk to Mayesville. You'll be tuckered out if you don't eat your breakfast."

"I'd be so scared I couldn't eat either," said Dolly. "Are you scared, Janie?"

"I don't know," Mary Jane answered slowly.

"I've never gone anywhere alone, but I'm not really scared! I'm not a bit scared!"

"Of course you're not!" Sis Liz said.

Her grandmother rocked back and forth in her chair by the stove. "My grandchild is going to school. There wasn't any school for me, nor for your mother and father. We were slaves, and it was a sin for anyone to teach us reading. You are lucky to have been born free so you can go to school and learn to read."

Willie came and stood by his sister. He held his hands behind his back. "Janie," he began. She turned to look at him and saw that he was bothered about something.

Suddenly he thrust out his hands. He was holding his shoes. They were heavy, copper-toed shoes which had been given to him by one of the white women for whom his mother did washing and ironing. He seldom let anyone touch them, for they were prized possessions.

"Here, Janie, take these. You don't want to go off to school barefooted."

Tears stung her eyelids. "Do you mean it, Willie? Do you want me to wear them?"

"Sure I do. Put them on, Janie."

With a shoe in each hand, she flung her arms around her brother and hugged him. Then she sat down on the little worn leather stool by her grandmother and thrust her bare feet into the stiff shoes. When she stood up, her feet, unaccustomed to shoes, felt strange.

"Here's your slate and something for your dinner, Janie." Her mother handed her a small tin pail filled with grits and a hunk of corn pone. "You'll be hungry at noontime."

With the pail in one hand and her slate in the other, Janie looked at her family. For a brief second she wondered if she would ever see them again. Then she grinned.

"Good-by! Good-by!" she said and went out

the door into the gray light of early morning. Her parents and brothers and sisters came to the door to watch her walk, straight-shouldered, head up, away from them and the cabin.

"She's mighty little to go off alone like that!" her father said.

"But she's strong," Patsy declared proudly. "She'll make it."

Mary Jane did not look back. She went steadily on, straight down the road to Mayesville. The October sky was beginning to be streaked with the rose and gold of dawn.

The air was sweet and cool. Along the roadside there were many flowers, including purple wild asters, yellow goldenrod, and sunflowers. Mary Jane thought she would like to stop and pick a bouquet for Miss Wilson, but she didn't have time. She could not be late.

The sun was well up by the time she came to the first houses of the town. Her father had told her how to get to the cabin where the school was held. A colored family that lived in the cabin had loaned Miss Wilson the use of a small room for her school.

"Just follow the road till you come to the railroad tracks," Sam had told Mary Jane. "Watch out for trains. Then cross over. It's the first house on the other side of the tracks."

Before Mary Jane crossed the shining rails she looked both ways to see whether a train was coming. Sometimes, when she had been in Mayesville with her parents, she had seen the snorting iron monster crossing the street. When she saw and heard nothing, she crossed the tracks, and there ahead of her was the cabin.

It was a small wooden building with a porch across the front. Around it was a clean-swept yard with large white stones at the edges. And there, standing on the porch and shading her eyes with one hand, was Miss Wilson.

She seemed to be looking for Mary Jane. The excited girl ran, stumbling in her heavy shoes, and came breathless to the porch.

Miss Wilson smiled at her. "Mary Jane Mc-Leod! Welcome to our school. Come on in. You'll have time to rest and get your breath before the others arrive."

She put an arm across the little girl's shoulder and led her inside. With a thumping heart Mary Jane stood and stared all about the room. This was school, where folks learned how to read. How lucky she was to be here!

The room was bare, but the walls and floor were clean. Long planks, resting on chunks of wood, served as benches. These benches were of different heights, the lowest ones in front, the highest at the back. On the front wall was a large black panel or square. Mary Jane stood there, not knowing what she was expected to do. She looked inquiringly at the teacher.

"Take a seat on that front bench, Mary Jane," Miss Wilson said. "You are larger and older than the other beginners in school, but I am sure you'll soon move back with the pupils who have been here longer. Anyone as eager to learn as you are will learn fast."

Mary Jane went to the first bench and sat down. It was so low her knees seemed to stick up in the air, but she didn't mind. She was in school, and if this was the first step in learning to read, it was all right with her.

The other children began to come in. They came with the assurance of familiarity, laughing and talking, shoving each other with good-natured teasing. They stared at the new pupil, but she pretended not to see them.

Miss Wilson picked up a small brass bell and went to the porch. She shook the bell and it made a pleasant, ringing sound. Then a few more children came rushing in, pell-mell.

Miss Wilson went to the front of the room. She clapped her hands together, and the whispering and giggling stopped. Mary Jane looked closely at the teacher, but her heart was beating out a little song,

> "I am in school! I am in school!
> I am going to read ! I am going to read!"

"Children," Miss Wilson said, "today we have a new pupil, Mary Jane McLeod. I know you will make her welcome to our Mayesville school. Now let us pray."

Suddenly Mary Jane felt right at home. Why, school wasn't at all scary. It was just like home or church. The children stood and Mary Jane stood with them. They repeated the Lord's Prayer, and her voice was clear and strong, for this was something she knew very well.

After the prayer the children sang, and this, too, was something Mary Jane knew.

"I think when I read that sweet story of old,
    When Jesus was here among men,
    How he called little children like lambs to
        the fold,
    I should like to have been with him then."

When the song was finished, the children sat
down on the benches again. Mary Jane, watching them, sat down, too. Miss Wilson gave her
a special smile, and she smiled back. Now she
was sure she was going to like school.

Mary Jane
Leads Out

MARY JANE sat up straight on her bench. She watched and listened and waited for her first lesson. For a while Miss Wilson devoted all her time to the older children, who sat in the back of the room. The half-dozen pupils who sat in the front of the room waited, wiggling and whispering.

Mary Jane wondered exactly what was going on behind her. She listened with all her might but could not make out what the teacher was doing. She knew the pupils were busy. Some had slates, like hers, and were scratching away on them. The pencils made a grating sound that set her teeth aching. Others had bits of charred stick in their hands and were making black marks on shingles they held on their knees.

The largest pupils of all were reading, actually reading, from a book they passed from one to another. They did not read easily, as the preacher did from the Bible. They stumbled over some words, but they were reading!

Miss Wilson seemed to be everywhere, correcting a reader, helping someone with his writing, passing out strips cut from a newspaper. Everything was orderly, and yet it was confusing to Mary Jane. She wished Miss Wilson would come and show her how to read.

Finally the teacher came to the bench where Mary Jane sat. She stood in front of the pupils and held up a small shingle which had been whittled into an odd shape. "Can you tell me what this is?" she asked.

"A," shouted the children.

"Very good!" She looked at Mary Jane. "The first thing we have to do in learning to read is to learn the letters of the alphabet. The first letter is A. Try to remember what it looks like. There are twenty-six letters in the alphabet. Do you know how many twenty-six is?"

Mary Jane looked at her hands. She could count to ten, because she had ten fingers. Her mother had taught her that, but twenty-six was beyond her understanding.

"Never mind, Mary Jane," Miss Wilson said. "You will learn that later. Now look at this letter A to see how it's shaped. Can you make a letter A on your slate?"

That was easy. Mary Jane's slate pencil made a scratching sound, and there, on her slate were some marks which represented her first attempt to write. The little children nearby, who had only charcoal and shingles, watched her and tried to copy the letter.

Miss Wilson held up two other letters cut from shingles. "B!" shouted the children, and "C!" The teacher stood these on the floor in front of the pupils. "Practice writing them," she said, and went back to the older pupils.

Mary Jane was excited about learning these letters, but she was disappointed about learning them so easily. She not only learned things readily, but she never had trouble remembering. She remembered all the hymns at church from beginning to end. She could repeat Bible stories almost exactly as she had heard them.

Even though she knew what the letters looked like, she had some difficulty copying them on her slate. Somehow she had little skill in writing. The seven-year-old girl sitting next to her could make prettier letters than Mary Jane's. Still she worked at it.

Miss Wilson came and looked at her slate. "You are starting well, but you can write easier if you hold your pencil this way." The teacher took the pencil in her own hand and showed how to hold it. Mary Jane said, "Thank you, Miss Wilson," and tried again.

She was still trying to make perfect letters when the teacher said, "It is time for recess, children. Lay aside your work."

What was recess? There was rattling and shuffling as the children put down their work. Next all of them stood up, and Mary Jane stood up, too. The teacher said, "Dismissed!" and the children made a rush for the door.

Mary Jane followed them and stood on the porch to look about. The older boys had a ball of rags wound into a sphere and held together by a cover of netted twine, which they had obtained by unraveling a gunny sack. They went off to one side of the yard and began throwing the ball from one to another. The girls and smaller boys just stood around quietly. Some were talking, some watched the boys, but most of them seemed to have nothing to do.

Mary Jane thought a minute. Then she ran out into the yard. "Look!" she called out in her clear, strong voice. "Let's play a game!"

Some of the children stopped talking and listened. One girl, just about Mary Jane's age, said, "We don't know any game."

"I'll show you one, a sort of cat-and-mouse game. You all pretend you're mice and choose some of those big rocks for your mouseholes. I'll be the cat. To start the game you come out of your holes and begin to play. Then I'll come running and try to catch you, but you scoot for your holes as fast as possible. If you get there before I catch you, you're safe. But if I catch you, I'll eat you up."

Some of the smaller children looked scared. One little boy dug his fist into his eyes. "I'm afraid to play," he whimpered.

Mary Jane laughed. "I won't really eat you, but if you're afraid, we'll play the game another way. If I catch you, you can be a cat and help me catch others. Let's try it."

Essie Lou Betts caught on at once. She was a

bright little girl who wanted to make friends with Mary Jane. She was as thin and wiry as Mary Jane was stout and sturdy.

"Come on!" she yelled, and ran toward a rock. "This is my mousehole." Two or three others chose rocks. The rest just stood and watched. Mary Jane ran around behind the cabin.

"Come out and play," Essie Lou called to the other mice. She left her rock and began to dance around the yard, waving her arms and shouting. The others followed her, yelling and dancing here and there. They had so much fun and made so much noise that they didn't see Mary Jane slip softly around the corner of the porch and start toward them.

Essie Lou screamed, "Cat! Cat!" and started for her rock. The others scattered, shrieking. Mary Jane could easily have caught a couple of the children, but she pretended to stumble and let them reach safety.

When she dashed behind the cabin, some of those who had just been watching decided to join the game. This time when Mary Jane chased the children, she caught Essie Lou, who had really wanted to be caught. The others screamed in pretended terror. Now there were two cats to chase all the mice.

By the time Miss Wilson rang the little bell to call the children back in to classes, most of them were running and screeching and having a fine time. Mary Jane and Essie Lou had become fast friends.

"You're my first real friend!" Mary Jane said as they ran, hand in hand, toward the porch. "My brother's a sort of friend, but you're the first friend outside my family."

"You're my first friend, too," Essie Lou said. "I don't have any brothers and sisters. We'll stick together, won't we?"

They rushed into the schoolroom, panting

from their game. Miss Wilson smiled at Mary Jane. "I saw you teaching the others that game, Mary Jane. Where did you learn to play it?"

"I didn't. I just made it up because I thought we should do something."

Her teacher patted her head. "You are going to be a great help to me." Then she murmured, "Some seem born to be leaders."

At noontime Mary Jane and Essie Lou ate their lunch together, sitting on the big rocks at one side of the schoolyard. After they finished, the children crowded around, ready to play. "Cat and mouse," they cried. "Cat and mouse."

Mary Jane looked at her new friend and giggled. "Do you suppose we're going to have to play cat and mouse all our spare time?"

"I reckon so, unless you think up something else. It's our first game here."

"I'll certainly try," Mary Jane promised.

Learning and Sharing

WILLIE CAME down the road to meet his sister as she came home from her first day at school. She had taken off the heavy shoes and was carrying one in each hand. Her feet, unaccustomed to shoes, felt better now.

"Did you learn how to read?" Willie asked.

Mary Jane shook her head. "No, not in one day, but I have started. It will take a while."

He turned and went loping ahead of her. "Just as I thought. School isn't any good. You've been gone a whole day and can't read."

"I've started, I tell you! I've learned to know some letters."

Mary Jane followed her brother into the cabin. The family gathered around her. "How was school?" "Did you like it?" "What did you do?" The questions flew around her.

"Yes, but she can't read yet!" said Willie.

"Stop talking, Willie," said his mother, "and let Janie do the talking."

Mary Jane put her lunch pail and her slate on the table. She sat down on a chair for a moment, because she was tired. She had walked five miles to school and five miles back. She had worked hard at her lessons and she had played hard at recess and noon. Soon she jumped up from the chair and started to explain.

"School was good. I liked it. I learned some letters and I showed the other children how to play a game. I made a friend named Essie Lou Betts. Miss Wilson said I was doing well."

"The child's tired and hungry!" Old Sophie interrupted. "Feed her and then she can share more of her learning with us. Thank goodness my grandchild is learning to read!"

"Your grandmother is right," Patsy agreed. "Supper's ready. Sit down and eat."

During the evening Mary Jane told her family about the letters she had learned. She drew them on her slate. She tried to teach the others, just as Miss Wilson had taught her. She had them repeat the names of the letters after her several times.

Some of them were rather confused by the lesson, but they tried. The two little girls, Dolly and the baby, went to sleep and Willie wasn't much interested. All the others, however, tried to do as Mary Jane asked.

"Learning letters is important because words are made up of letters," Mary Jane explained. "You have to learn these letters before you can read. Altogether there are twenty-six letters used in making up words."

117

Finally her father said, "That's enough for tonight, Janie. Wash your feet and go to bed. You've another long day ahead of you."

Mary Jane put her slate aside and went out to the big tub on the back porch. As she scrubbed her feet she thought about her new friend. She loved her sisters, but it was nice to have another girl, a new girl, to talk with and share her ideas with. Essie Lou was going to be fun to know. Seeing her was another thing to look forward to every day.

That night Sam McLeod gave thanks for the opportunity his daughter was having, the opportunity to learn things that had not been possible for him. Mary Jane was thankful for her school and her new friends.

Mary Jane fell into the routine of going to school early in the morning, spending the day at school, coming home at dusk, and sharing her lessons with the family after supper. She did

118

not mind the long walk every morning, because school and Miss Wilson were at the other end. And she did not mind the long walk in the evening because she knew that her home and family were waiting for her there.

A few weeks after she had started to school, she came home one evening with a new light shining in her dark eyes. "I have a real surprise for you, Mama! I've been promoted!"

"What does that mean, child?" her mother asked. "What has happened to you?"

"Miss Wilson has moved me back with the older girls. Now I sit with Essie Lou, and she has been in school much longer than I have. Besides, Essie Lou could read a little when she came. Her father learned how to read when he was a soldier at Charleston, and he taught her some of the letters. But now I have caught up with her and can study with her."

"Can you read yet?" Willie asked.

"Yes, I can read a little and I can make all the letters on my slate. I can write whole words, too. Shall I write my name?"

The McLeods gathered close and Janie scratched out on her slate, "MARY JANE MCLEOD." Sam McLeod touched the letters with a gnarled black finger. "Would you like to know how you got your name, Janie?" he asked.

She nodded and he explained. "When we were slaves, we didn't really have names that we chose for ourselves. Our masters gave us names, but only first names, like my name, Sam, and your mother's name, Patsy. People round about called me Henry McLeod's Sam or something like that, rather than Sam McLeod. Then, when Mr. Lincoln set us all free, everything was changed. From then on we have had two names, first and last names the same as white folks.

"Most of us took the name of the family that had owned us. Henry McLeod owned us, so we just took that name. Now you can write it there, plain, for anyone to see. It surely makes me proud to see it."

"Do you have real books in school?" asked Mary Jane's mother.

"Miss Wilson has a book which she lets pupils read, one after another. I haven't learned enough yet to read from the book. Mostly she has us read big print which she cuts out of newspapers. Sometimes she pastes some of the words together to make a sort of story. But it's real reading, almost as good as from a book."

"Maybe someday we can get a book."

"We have a book, Mama, and someday I'll be able to read it. I promise I will."

The days grew shorter and colder. Now it was pitch dark when Mary Jane left for school and dark when she came home. Her mother worried about the cold. One day, when it was raining, she brought out Willie's old coat.

"Here, put on this old coat," she said to Janie. "It's not pretty and it's a little too big for you, but it will keep off the rain."

Mary Jane put on the coat. "It's warm."

"If anyone makes fun of it——"

"Oh, Mama," Mary Jane interrupted, "nobody will, because it's just as good as anyone else has. Some of the children have to stay home on these cold days because they don't have any coat at all. I'm mighty grateful for this."

Old Sophie, rocking by the warm stove, pulled off the old gray shawl she always had about her shoulders. "Here, child, wrap this shawl around your head. It's old, but it's warm."

"Oh, no, Grandma! You'll be cold!"

"Please take it, child. I don't want to let you go forth in the cold while I sit here, snug and warm. Anyhow, just knowing that you are getting some schooling warms me enough. It warms me through and through."

In spite of coat and shawl, Mary Jane was almost frozen before she reached the school. Her bare hands were so stiff from carrying her lunch pail and slate that she thought she would never be able to use them again. When she entered the room, Miss Wilson took the cold hands into her own warm palms and gently rubbed them until they were warm and limber again.

Mary Jane accepted the teacher's attention without questioning. To her, the extra kindness was all a part of school, of learning. She had so little experience mingling with people outside her own family that she took whatever came as a matter of course.

"I thought you might not come today, so far in the storm!" Miss Wilson said.

Mary Jane shook her head. "I couldn't stay at home. I might miss something."

Miss Wilson chuckled. "What a fine record! Some pupils don't need the excuse of a storm to stay at home, let alone a five-mile walk! But you have never missed a day."

"I don't want to. There's so much I have to learn before school closes next summer. I want to learn all that I can."

By the time closing day came, Mary Jane could read as well as any other pupil in the school. She forged ahead in reading, even though she had problems in writing and spelling. Learning to read was what she wanted most.

In the spring Mary Jane hated to say good-by to her teacher, Essie Lou, and all the other boys and girls. "It's plowing time," she explained, "and Papa needs me to help. I wish we could go to school all summer."

"So do I," said Miss Wilson, "but we'd be worn out, if we went to school all the time during summer and winter."

"I wouldn't," said Mary Jane.

The teacher put her arm around Mary Jane

124

and said, "You'll be back again as soon as your father sells his cotton next fall. In the meantime take this little blue-backed speller home with you to study. Then next fall you may be as good in spelling as you are in reading."

Mary Jane liked Miss Wilson's words of encouragement and said, "I'll surely try, Miss Wilson. Thank you."

The children found it hard to say good-by. "If you only lived down our road, we might see each other sometimes," Mary Jane said to Essie Lou. "Or if we went to the same church we might see each other. Now it'll be a long time till we get a chance to be together."

"I surely hope you'll be back to school next fall, Mary Jane. Promise me you'll come."

"I'll come if I can!" They clasped right hands, crossed their hearts and made the promises of lasting friendship.

In spite of Mary Jane's sadness at leaving

books and teacher and friends, she enjoyed working in the cotton patch again. During the soft, balmy spring of South Carolina, air and earth smelled sweet and fresh. Pale hepaticas pushed their stems up through the dead leaves under the trees, and the rosy blossoms of trailing arbutus gave off their lovely fragrance.

Mary Jane and Dolly liked to hunt for the first flowers of spring. A little later, they knelt beside certain blossoms to watch insects coming to collect nectar for honey. Every now and then they found an insect trying to escape from the sticky liquid in a blossom.

At times the two girls imitated insects and sucked sweet juice from some of the flowers. Both of them were happy and thankful to be out in the fields and woods in the early spring months of the year.

All the while there was work to be done. Sam McLeod hitched Old Bush to the plow and set

out for the cotton patch, with Mary Jane skipping along beside him. "Your job," he said, "is to take the guide rope and lead Old Bush along the furrows, straight across the field. You can see them, just the same as last year."

"Last year Willie led Old Bush!"

"That's right," said her father, "but this year Willie's too big to lead the mule and you must take his place."

"I'm glad," said Mary Jane. "I'm proud of Willie and happy to take his place so that he can do heavier work."

"I know you are, child. You're a good helper in the family and we're mighty fortunate to have you. I don't know what we would do without you. Now let's get to the plowing."

Mary Jane took her place at the mule's head. She picked up the guide rope and started down the furrow between the dry stalks of last year's cotton plants. These would soon be uprooted

128

and new seeds planted in their place. The fresh earth felt good to her bare feet. She had not enjoyed the brogans and wondered how white folks managed to wear shoes all the time. Her feet were now freed from shoes just as her parents had been freed from slavery. The idea brought to her mind one of her grandmother's favorite hymns. The old woman had said, "When we sang this song, we were scared we'd be tossed into jail. Some of the slaves were."

To think of a hymn was to sing it, and Mary Jane lifted her head and sang,

> "O, Father, how long
> Must us poor sinners suffer here?
> Well, it won't be long,
> For the Lord will call us home.
> We'll soon be free——"

Her father joined in the singing. Mary Jane looked back. She saw that her father was as happy as she was. He grasped the curved handles of the plow with his gnarled black hands. His bare feet made prints in the new-turned earth. His head flung back, he sang joyfully.

"I don't know what part of cotton raising I like best, plowing or picking, maybe, but not weed chopping," Mary Jane called back.

Her father chuckled. "Weed chopping is purely work, and I reckon it's nobody's favorite job. It's work that must be done, though, aching back or no aching back!"

Together they burst into another song.

"'Way down yonder in the cotton patch—
   Oh, my aching back!
Chopping weeds in the summer sun,
   Oh, my aching back."

Old Bush stepped along as lively as if he enjoyed the song. The leaves and the grass, wet with dew, sparkled in the sun. The earth smelled good. Mary Jane was happy.

Reading Proves Worthwhile

ONE SUMMER evening, after Mary Jane had washed for supper, she lifted the front cover of the big Bible and looked inside. The first page was decorated in red and blue and yellow and the second and third pages were white. None of these pages contained any words.

As Mary Jane looked, she wondered why these pages that could have been filled with glowing words were empty. Then she came to a page that said, in large black letters,

THE HOLY BIBLE

CONTAINING

THE OLD AND NEW TESTAMENTS

This was what she wanted! Her heart thumped. She was actually reading the Good Book. Tonight, when the time came for evening prayers, she would show everybody she could read. She turned to the table of contents which listed the titles of all the books she had heard the preacher name many times. Slowly she went down the list, sounding each title carefully.

Sometimes there was a title that especially pleased her because she remembered an interesting story about it. Joshua fought the battle of Jericho! She hoped to read this book someday. Samuel was her father's name. She must read this book, too. She certainly was grateful that she could read with her own eyes.

That evening she quivered with excitement when she said anxiously, "Papa, would you like me to read from the Bible?"

Everyone looked at her. "Can you really read from the Bible?" asked her father. "We surely will be pleased to hear you read. Sit here by the candle while I bring the Book!"

Sam McLeod carried the Bible reverently and placed it on her knees. "Where shall I read, Papa?" she asked in great excitement.

Mary Jane's grandmother edged the old rocking chair close. She was murmuring over and over, "Hallelujah! Praise the Lord!"

Sam McLeod did not hesitate. "This is a new thing for us all," he said. "It's a beginning. Why not start at the beginning? Start right at the first of the Good Book, like we're starting a new kind of life."

Mary Jane was a little disappointed because her favorite story was about Queen Esther. She had hoped her father would suggest this one, but he was right. Since this was a new experience, she should start at the beginning. Slowly she turned the pages until she came to GENESIS.

Bending low over the page, with the candle

133

flame flickering on the small print, she began to read. "In the beginning God created the heaven and the earth," she read clearly. "And the earth was without form, and void; and darkness was upon the face of the deep."

Old Sophie, listening closely to the reading, could scarcely contain her joy. "Thank the Lord! My own grandchild is reading the Good Book." Then she began to sing.

> "We're on our way and we won't turn back!
> We're on our way! We're on our way!
> We're on our way to Canaan's land!
> We're on our way! We're on our way!"

All members of the family joined in and sang with special fervor. Mary Jane thought that her grandmother had chosen a very good song to sing at this time, when something new was happening in the McLeod cabin.

When they finished singing, Mary Jane continued reading. The members of the family

134

watched and drank in the words, knowing that now, every evening, they could hear the precious messages that meant so much to them.

The news spread rapidly that Sam McLeod's little girl could read the Good Book. One by one, neighboring Negroes dropped by the cabin to look at Mary Jane and, perhaps, to hear her read. Her grandmother beamed whenever Mary Jane's name was mentioned. Even Willie looked at her with more respect than he had ever shown. When there was a yard meeting, Mary Jane was always called upon to read to the congregation.

During the latter part of the summer, while the cotton bolls were forming and filling, the Negroes led more leisurely lives. At this time, partly due to Mary Jane's Bible reading, the people of the neighborhood held many outdoor meetings. Itinerant or traveling preachers started to hold camp meetings in many parts of the South. One famous preacher, J.W.E. Brown of Atlanta, Georgia, held camp meetings at Sumter, South Carolina. He was famous not only as a preacher but also as a missionary. Sam McLeod heard about the meetings and decided to take his family to hear Reverend Brown.

He placed a thick layer of straw in the wagon box and hitched Old Bush to the wagon. The members of the family piled in, long before daylight, for the long ride to the city. Besides attending the camp meeting they planned to visit a married daughter Sally, who lived in Sumter. Mary Jane was especially excited.

The family had a joyous reunion at Sally's home, with fried chicken and watermelon as special treats. Then it was time to go to the camp meeting, which was held in a tent at the edge of town. As the McLeods made their way down the street, Mary Jane thought she had never seen so many people. Dolly clutched her sister's hand, frightened by the confusion of what seemed to

136

her to be a great city. The size of the crowd increased as they came to the tent.

Inside the tent, the ground was covered with sawdust and there were rows of planks for people to sit on. At the front, there was a raised platform, decorated with bright bunting. The two little girls found places near the front and sat looking at the platform and wondering what would happen.

The meeting began with the usual prayer and hymns, after which Reverend Brown mounted the platform. Mary Jane had never seen anyone so handsome or so gorgeously dressed. Even the white folks in Mayesville didn't have such black coats with long tails, gleaming white shirts, or sparkling black shoes.

Reverend Brown had a strong, appealing voice, which reached listeners in all parts of the tent. Mary Jane listened to every word he said.

She sat entranced as he told of Africa, of the

plight of the black people there, her grandmother's people, who had never heard of God and Christ and the Holy Bible. They were heathen, he declared, heathen in need of salvation. He called for missionaries to take up the work, to go to Africa and carry the gospel and salvation to these unfortunate people.

Mary Jane took hold of Dolly's arm. In her excitement she squeezed her arm so hard that the little girl flinched and started to whimper. "Listen, Dolly," said Mary Jane. "Reverend Brown wants us to become missionaries in Africa. When I grow up, I'm going to be a missionary! I'm going to help save those people."

She left the meeting in such an exalted state that she could scarcely hear the ordinary talk of the family. Her mother noticed her excited actions and her shining eyes. "What's happened to you, child?" she asked.

"I'm going to be a missionary in Africa when

I grow up!" Mary Jane said. "I'm going to take salvation to the heathen!"

"Hallelujah!" exclaimed Old Sophie, hobbling along beside her daughter. She pounded on the ground with her cane. "Somehow I knew my grandchild was going to be great!"

Willie looked at his sister. "You'd better wait a while," he told her. "You'd better wait a few years."

When the McLeods returned home, the bolls in the cotton patch were white. It was cotton picking time again. This year, like the year before, the crop was good. Sam and Willie piled the old wagon box high with heavy sacks to go to the cotton gin. Janie came out to climb up behind her father and brother. "What's that you're carrying?" Sam asked his daughter.

"This is my slate," replied Janie. "I'm taking it along to write some figures."

"Why? What do you plan to do?"

"I thought I'd write down how many pounds of cotton we have this year," said Janie excitedly. "Won't that be something good to know?"

Sam hesitated. "I don't know, Janie. I just don't know. We've never done this before."

"What hurt can it do?" asked Janie pleadingly. "Why have I learned to read and write and cipher, if I can't use what I have learned?"

Her father was still worried, but he said no more. When they reached the yard beside the cotton gin building, Mary Jane helped her father and Willie unload the sacks. Then, slate in hand, she went and stood by the scales. Clem Hastings hung a sack on the hook and moved the brass weight along the black arm. "Just over two hundred pounds, Sam!" he said, and started to write the number in his book.

Mary Jane was already watching. She felt her heart thumping, but she said, "Wasn't that nearly three hundred pounds, Mr. Hastings?"

The man looked at her with a sharp questioning glance. Then he bent closer to the scale and said, "You're right, child! It is nearly three hundred pounds, two hundred and eighty, to be exact." He sounded surprised, and his face was red. Mary Jane wrote "280" on her slate.

When Hastings weighed the next sack, Mary Jane stepped close, peered at the number on the scale arm, and wrote the weight down. The man frowned and stared at her. "Do you think I'm cheating you?" he asked.

"No sir, Mr. Hastings, but my father needs to know how much cotton he raises, so I want to help him find out. He lets me go to school when I could be working at home, so I want to use what I learn to help him."

"I heard about that school, but I think it's a mistake to have a school just for Negroes. They don't need an education."

Mary Jane didn't answer Hastings, but she

had a reply in mind. "We can use it to keep folks from cheating us."

When all the sacks were weighed, Hastings asked, "Did you learn how to figure? Can you add up all those numbers?"

"If there aren't too many numbers and I am careful, I can add them. I'm one of the best pupils in numbers at my school."

"What's the South coming to?" asked Hastings. "I've never heard of anything like this happening in the South before. What's the South coming to, anyway?"

When he handed Sam the slip of paper with the figures on it, Mary Jane took it from her father's hand and compared the figures with what she'd written. Hastings watched closely and said, "You won't find anything wrong."

Mary Jane said nothing, for he was right. The figures matched perfectly, and when she added her columns, the amount was the same as his.

It was surprisingly large. She was sure it was more than they had ever had before.

When Mary Jane and her father went to the office, the clerk stared at the paper. "What's this, Sam? It looks as if you've had a bumper crop this year. Clem didn't make a mistake in his figuring, did he?"

"No," Sam answered quietly. "My daughter here checked his figures."

The clerk frowned. He went out the door but soon returned, scowling, and started to count out the money. Mary Jane watched closely, but she couldn't tell whether or not he counted correctly because she lacked experience in counting money. Still, she watched as if to pretend that she knew what he was doing. Her eyes nearly popped out of her head when she saw him place two gold coins beside the silver dollars. Never before had the family had any gold money.

Sam seemed to take everything calmly. He

picked up the money, stuffed it into his pockets, thanked the clerk, and walked out with Mary Jane. When they got into the wagon, Sam could hold his excitement in check no longer. He took out the money and showed it to Willie.

"We've got more money this year than ever before, even two gold coins," he said.

Willie stared at the shining yellow coins. "How did you get them, Papa?"

"Your sister got them. It surely pays to be able to read. We found that out today."

Willie looked from the glittering money to Mary Jane. He shook his head in wonder. "I never before thought reading was worth the trouble," he said.

"Well, it surely is!" said his sister. "Not only that, it's fun, too."

Graduation Day

"Tomorrow will be the proudest day of my life," declared Patsy McLeod. "It will be Janie's graduation day."

She was speaking to her husband one evening in the spring of 1887. All the McLeod children were in bed. Only Patsy and Sam were still up. Patsy was ironing the frills on the white dress she had made for Mary Jane.

Her husband smiled. "Are you prouder than you were on the day of emancipation?"

"That was a very joyful day, too," said Patsy, using a thick cloth pad to protect her hand as she took the iron to the stove.

146

She picked up a hotter iron and went back to the dress. "Yes, I appreciated the day of emancipation, but somehow tomorrow will be better, because we'll celebrate something we've earned for ourselves. Emancipation freed us from the bondage of our bodies, but now our child is freed from the bondage of ignorance."

Mary Jane came out of the bedroom in her short cotton nightshirt. "I just can't get to sleep, Mama. I keep thinking about tomorrow."

"That's natural, child," Patsy told her. "It'll be a big day for sure."

Mary Jane touched the frills around the yoke of the dress. "They're pretty, Mama, I never expected to have such a pretty dress."

"Mrs. McIntosh was good to give us the cloth. She seems to be almost as proud that you have finished your schooling as we are."

Patsy held up a wide, pale blue ribbon sash. "Your sister Sally sent this over from Sumter.

She's coming to the celebration tomorrow. It will be a proud day for the family."

Mary Jane went back into the bedroom, but she didn't think she would ever get to sleep. For three years, now, she had looked forward to the day when she would graduate.

Miss Wilson had held up graduation from Mayesville Institute as a shining goal for all the pupils. She had encouraged them to attend day after day, year after year, until they could finish the course outlined by the sponsors of the school. Only six pupils had completed the course, and tomorrow they would receive diplomas in the first graduation exercises ever held.

The thought of the school made Mary Jane shiver with excitement. She had watched it grow and change. Miss Wilson had been such a good teacher and had inspired so many Negro children to attend, that the mission board had built a new yellow brick building for the school.

148

Now the children had real seats and desks, real books, real pencils and paper, and a real blackboard instead of the makeshift equipment with which the school had started.

"I like the school now, but I'll never forget that first day," Mary Jane said to herself. "It's nice to have all the new things, but it was possible to learn without them."

She smiled drowsily, remembering the long walks she had taken to and from school. "I figure I have walked about four thousand miles or more, barefoot most of the time, but I have been glad to do it. I'd walk twice that far, if I had to, just to get a little learning."

The next morning Mary Jane, dressed in the new white dress, looked into the bit of mirror that still hung by the door. "I've surely grown a lot," she said, grinning at herself in the mirror. "I'm as big and strong as Josie Lewis, and she's seventeen. I've changed in other ways, too. I have no little braids now, no gingham dress, and no scratchy slate."

"You don't have any copper-toed shoes, either," said Willie, coming to stand beside his sister. He was dressed up in his best clothes to attend the exercises.

Mary Jane turned from the mirror to smile at her brother. "My, how my feet hurt in those shoes, but I'm grateful that you gave them to me. They helped me get an education."

"Come on, folks. It's time to get going!" Sam McLeod called from the yard.

Patsy and Mary Jane helped Old Sophie into a rocking chair that they had placed in the wagon box for her. The other members of the family found places on quilts that had been put on the wagon box floor to protect their clothes. All were dressed in their very best, as was fitting for such a day.

Mary Jane in her white frills and Patsy in her

purple polka dot dress, were squeezed together on the seat beside Sam. "See all those people!" Mary Jane exclaimed. "Everybody in the county seems to be going to Mayesville!"

She was right. The fact that the Mayesville Institute for Negro children was holding graduation exercises had attracted wide attention. Both Negroes and white folks for miles around wondered what the exercises would be like and were curious to see them.

The program was to be held outdoors. The pupils had set up a platform for the prominent men of the town, the members of the school board, and the sponsoring church. The children had decorated this stand with greens and flowers, a bit wilted by the spring sunshine, but still bright enough to add color to the scene. There were long rows of plank benches for the audience in front of the platform.

Sam tied Old Bush to the fence rail and the

family joined the crowd in the schoolyard. Sally, with her youngsters, came toward them. "Hello, Mama and Papa." She kissed her grandmother and turned to Mary Jane. "I'm proud of you, Sister. You are the first McLeod to get a school diploma, but my Louis will graduate from the Sumter school next year and my other children later. We surely are getting educated."

"I have to sit up front, so I'll leave you here," Mary Jane explained. "When I give my speech, I'll be looking at you."

"And we'll be looking right back at you," her sister said gayly.

Mary Jane went to the front row of seats and took her place between Essie Lou and Josie Lewis. Hester Jackson sat next to Essie Lou and the two boys of the class huddled together.

"I'm scared!" Josie whispered. "I've never been so scared in all my life as I am right now. Look at those men up there on the platform.

152

Even the mayor is there. See that man in the high silk hat. Who is he?"

"That man is from the mission board, up North. Miss Wilson told us he was coming, but I guess you were too scared to remember."

"Aren't you really scared at all?" Essie Lou asked eagerly.

"No, I don't think I am," replied Mary Jane. "I'm a funny sort of person. I guess I like to talk too much to become scared."

The exercises began with a prayer and hymns. The familiar routine eased some of the tension the graduates were feeling. Then the visiting celebrities gave long and boring talks, which were happily interspersed with more hymns. All the while the sun climbed higher and higher in the sky. The pupils in their unaccustomed finery began to sweat.

At last the time came for the graduates to take part. According to custom, the two boys were placed ahead of the girls on the program. Jim Greene stammered through his speech, received his diploma, and returned to his seat. The audience clapped loudly.

Now it was Hank Gleason's turn to speak. Hank was an overgrown, awkward fellow, eighteen years old. He was the poorest pupil in the class, but his mother, by sheer determination, had forced him to attend school.

Mary Jane and Essie Lou watched Hank rise awkwardly to his feet. They had often seen his mother, a tiny little woman, drag him unwillingly to school. Now sweat stood out on his forehead, and he paused momentarily as if wondering what to do. He seemed too dazed and frightened to make his speech.

Finally he walked clumsily up the steps to the platform. Then he tripped and sprawled across the floor in front of the visiting speakers. Laughter rippled through the audience.

Mary Jane was angry. She thought it was rude for people to laugh at Hank because he had an accident. Hank's mother stood up, ready to help him, but he soon climbed to his feet. Then he lumbered to the front of the platform and began to mumble the speech which Miss Wilson had helped him to prepare.

Hank mumbled so badly that it was almost impossible to make out his words, but he kept on talking. When he finished, he grabbed his diploma and staggered back to his seat. Mary Jane and Essie Lou applauded him, and Hank's mother patted him on the back. She glistened with pride as she watched him.

"She ought to be proud!" Mary Jane whispered to Essie Lou. "He has had a harder time than anyone else in the class. We all should be proud that he has made it."

Now it was the girls' turn. Miss Wilson had listed them according to age, and Mary Jane, being the youngest, came last. When she mounted the platform, she was calm and assured. She felt nervous and trembled only when she reached out her hand for her diploma.

156

"You outshined them all!" Willie told her after the ceremony.

Folks gathered around, shaking her hand and saying nice things about her. She smiled and answered, but somewhere deep inside her was a feeling of sadness.

"They all act as if this is the end," she was thinking, "but I hope it is only the beginning! I don't want my education to end now. There's a new college for women in Columbia, but it's only for white women, so I can't go there. If only someone would start a college for Negro women, but I'm afraid it won't happen."

By now she felt like praying for more schooling, hoping that her prayer would be answered. "Dear Lord, You have brought me this far on my way to an education. Let me go on and on, so I can serve You better. You know how I want to go to Africa, to bring the heathen to Your arms. Let me be prepared, please, O Lord!"

When the people began to leave for home, Mary Jane hunted up Miss Wilson to tell her good-by. The teacher put an arm about her and said, "You have been my most promising pupil, but I see sadness in your eyes."

"I hate to think that my schooling is coming to an end," replied Mary Jane. "I'm afraid I can't stand it." Her voice shook, and tears started to come to her eyes.

"Don't give up hope, dear. Never give up hope. You are too rare a person to be forgotten, and you won't be."

Mary Jane nodded and tried to smile. "Thank you for all you've done for me," she said.

When she rejoined her family, after talking with Miss Wilson, she felt somewhat encouraged. "I don't know why, but I feel better," she thought. Then once more she smiled.

Another Chance

"Good-by! Good-by, Mayesville! Good-by, Mama and Papa, Grandma and Willie and Dolly and Hattie and Sis Liz. Good-by to everyone and everything I've ever known!"

Mary Jane looked out the dusty window of the railroad car and waved to the crowd of people who had come to see her off. The whistle blew, her friends shouted and waved, the wheels turned, and she was on her way.

"I'm not afraid, and I'm not going to cry," she said. "I'm just full of thanks that I have an opportunity to continue my schooling."

After the excitement of graduation, Mary

Jane had really given up hope of obtaining any further education. Also, she had found it necessary to work hard in the fields.

Old Bush, the faltering old mule, had died and she had taken the mule's place in pulling the plow. Actually, she hadn't minded this hard work very much because she was young and strong. In addition, she had worked beside her father, hoeing and picking cotton. She had tried to appear cheerful, but her heart was heavy.

"I had almost given up hope of becoming a missionary," she thought to herself. "I had almost settled down to being a field hand, as if I knew nothing better."

After Mary Jane had graduated, two hopeless years had passed, years in which she had tried to be contented. Then, one day, when she had almost resigned herself to her lot, Miss Emma Wilson had come again. She had come as a messenger of hope and opportunity.

"Mary Jane," Miss Wilson had said. "I have good news for you. You can continue your education and go on to high school! Listen to this!" Then she had told how a Quaker dressmaker, away out in Denver, Colorado, had sent money to pay for a year's scholarship at the Scotia Seminary in Concord, North Carolina.

"The mission board has let me choose the pupil to get this scholarship," Miss Wilson had added, "and, of course, I have chosen you. Earlier I had told you that we wouldn't forget you, and we haven't. I am so happy for you."

Mary Jane's parents had been delighted with this opportunity. Much as they had needed her at home, they had realized that she must be spared. All her white friends as well as the neighboring Negroes had been thrilled.

They were proud that a Negro girl from their county had been chosen to go to the Scotia Seminary, which was already becoming noted among the people of the South. All had pitched in to help her get ready for the opening of school that fall. Now they had come to the station at Mayesville to wish her well in her new undertaking.

Mary Jane turned from the window to look about her. She noted that most of the passengers in the car were white, but there were a few Negroes. She didn't have the slightest idea of how to act or what to do, so she decided to sit still and watch the others.

At noon she noticed that they began to open shoe boxes or paper sacks to eat their lunches. At once she unfolded a piece of cloth wrapped around some food and began to eat. Then in the afternoon she dozed briefly, but was suddenly awakened by the conductor calling, "Concord! Concord next stop!"

The time had passed quickly. Now Mary Jane wondered whether she could get all her things off the car when the train stopped. She

162

hastily collected her bundles and her cheap pasteboard suitcase and followed other passengers out to the vestibule to wait. When the train came to a halt she walked down the steps and stood on the wooden platform, staring about her.

Beside the platform was a low wooden building with two doors in front. One door was marked "White," and the other was marked "Colored." Mary Jane stared at the signs. She was used to the way Negroes were separated from white people, but on the train she had noted that black and white people had ridden together. It had made her think that things might be different outside Sumter County. Now she thought they must be the same everywhere.

A young white woman came toward her. "Are you Mary McLeod?" she asked. "I am Miss Bowers, a teacher at Scotia. I have come to welcome you and take you to the school."

"Thank you," was all Mary Jane could say.

A Negro man came up, picked up Mary Jane's belongings and took them to a buggy nearby. She followed the teacher to the vehicle, climbed in beside her, and soon was riding comfortably along a shady, dusty road.

While they were riding, Miss Bowers chatted cheerfully, and Mary Jane relaxed. She liked Miss Bowers very much, and soon started to tell her about the school at Mayesville, about Miss Wilson, and about the McLeod family.

Suddenly Miss Bowers interrupted and said, "There is the school, Mary." Ahead of them, in a grove of trees, stood a small group of buildings. They looked elegant, especially a three-story yellow brick building and a four-story red brick building which stood nearby.

"The yellow building is Graves Hall, where classes are held," Miss Bowers explained. "The other is Faith Hall where the girls eat and sleep. The chapel is there, too.

"First we'll go to your room so you can see where you'll live. Then you can wash away some of the grime you picked up on the train. Someday I hope train travel can be cleaner."

Mary Jane followed her into the building and stood staring at two curved flights of stairs which led upward and disappeared overhead. She had seen a stairway in the McIntosh home, but she had never climbed one of them. She was so interested in the gleaming steps that she scarcely noticed the rug on the floor, the lace curtains at the windows, and the polished tables and chairs standing about.

"Come, Mary," called Miss Bowers. "Your room is upstairs. I'll show you."

Miss Bowers started up the steps and Mary Jane followed. They went down the hall to a room with the door open. Inside, a white girl, somewhat older than Mary Jane, was studying, but she rose as Miss Bowers entered the room.

"Abbie," the teacher said, "this is your new roommate, Mary Jane McLeod, and Mary, this is Abbie Greely, who has been at Scotia for two years. She can help you get used to our ways of living here. I'm sure you'll enjoy knowing each other." She turned and left the room.

Mary Jane was temporarily surprised and speechless. She grinned at the white girl. "Hello! I'm certain that I'll need help."

Abbie smiled and said, "You may count on me." Already the two girls were friends.

Mary Jane was right about needing help. She needed help in knowing how to make the bed with its white sheets and blankets and pillow cases. She needed help in learning to use the washbasin in her room. "At home we have a big wooden tub on the back porch," she explained to Abbie. "We all wash in the one tub. I have never had a basin like this, all to myself."

She watched the other girls at supper time

166

and saw how they used their napkins and knives, forks, and spoons. She noticed how they helped themselves to portions of food from the bowls and platters which were passed. She had never been exposed to such things but caught on quickly. Before long, she was as much at home at Scotia as any other girl there.

For the next five years, from the time she was fourteen years old until she turned nineteen, Mary Jane lived at Scotia Seminary. She finished the course of study in three years and stayed on two years more as a teacher. In all that time, she never had a chance to visit her family, back in South Carolina.

As a student, Mary Jane had worked hard. She still hoped to be a missionary in Africa, so she put in long, extra hours studying the Bible. She felt that she must be thoroughly acquainted with the Bible in order to convert the people of Africa to Christianity.

She had taken great pride in doing the chores assigned to her at the seminary. It was necessary for every girl to help with the upkeep of the buildings, and she had carried out her assignments with enthusiasm. She was especially proud of making the stairs shine when it was her turn to keep them clean.

She had been a favorite with the girls, too. She had proved to be a leader, organizing teams and games and speech contests. She now had a rich contralto voice and belonged to all the choral groups in the school.

Besides carrying on such activities, she had done work outside the seminary, especially during the summer. Since she could not go home to help her family, she felt that she must assist indirectly by working here. So, whenever she could get an outside job, such as washing, ironing, cooking, or cleaning house, she took it and sent the money home to her family.

Now, at the age of nineteen, she had been accepted as a student at the Moody Bible Institute in Chicago. There she would receive further training for her work as a missionary. Prior to going away for another long period, however, she wanted to visit her family.

That summer, Mary Jane went back to Mayesville, but many people who met her on the street failed to recognize her. Now she was a fully-grown woman with upswept hair and an assured manner. Dressed in a straw hat, white shirtwaist, and black skirt, she looked little like the fourteen-year-old girl who had boarded the train several years before amid shouts of good wishes.

Mary Jane again walked the familiar road from Mayesville to the McLeod cabin. There her family knew her immediately, in spite of her changed appearance. She recognized her home, too, although the old cabin had burned down and a new plank cabin stood in its place.

By now her grandmother was so old and frail she scarcely ever left her old rocking chair without help. Her father, now in his sixties, was still straight and handsome, but he was wrinkled and gray. Her mother, too, showed signs of years of hard work. Sis Liz, Luke, and Willie were married. Hattie was a fast-growing girl of eleven, and Dolly was working as a full time maid for the McIntoshes.

"I wish I could stay, but I must go," Mary Jane said when she had to leave.

"I know," her mother answered. "You have helped us, and we have kept you in our hearts while you have been away. We have always been proud of you, and you are meant for bigger things than this cabin."

A School by a City Dump

AGAIN Mary Jane said good-by to her family to continue her schooling. This time she enrolled at Moody Bible Institute in Chicago. While there she trained for missionary work by going into saloons, slum districts, and even prisons to preach the gospel and sing.

Many of her friends said, "You are crazy to try to save the souls of those men. They are wicked through and through, and there is nothing you can do to save them."

While Mary Jane studied at Moody Bible Institute, she hoped to carry on missionary work in Africa, but when she finished her work in 1904, she had no opportunity to go there. Even so, she retained her religious zeal and decided to return to the South to teach among her own people. Each day after she finished teaching in classrooms, she went out into communities to preach and sing and to provide guidance in cleanliness, sanitation, and cooking.

She taught in Augusta, Georgia, and in Sumter near her home. Everywhere she attracted attention by her work with her own people, but there always were certain onlookers who said she was wasting her time.

In Sumter she met and married a teacher named Albertus Bethune. Later they moved to Savannah, Georgia, where their son Albert was born. Then they moved to Palatka, Florida, where Mrs. Bethune continued to teach.

"Why can't you be content just to teach and forget about doing missionary work on the side?" her husband asked her.

"Because I was born to be a missionary," Mrs. Bethune replied. "My people here in the South need help just as badly as the black people of Africa. The schools reach only a few families among them. Besides, most of the families need more than schools for their children in order to get along in the world."

While Mrs. Bethune was teaching at Palatka, she decided to start a school for Negro girls. She would teach the girls things they needed for everyday living, not just a skimpy version of courses offered white children.

She hoped to open her school in Daytona Beach, Florida. She had learned that a railroad and new hotels had been built there and that many Negroes had flocked to the city to work. She was sure that most of the families were living in unsanitary sheds and that their children were not going to school. This seemed to be an ideal place for her to start a school.

174

She talked her plan over with her husband, and they agreed to move to Daytona Beach. A few weeks later, she decided to pack her belongings and go on ahead with her five-year-old son. Now she and Albert were looking for a place to live in Daytona Beach.

"Look there, Albert," she said. "What do you think of that little house?" She pointed to a rickety, unpainted shack standing beside the city dump. It was empty and had a "For Rent" sign tacked on the front door.

Albert looked up at his mother. "Is that where we are going to live?" he asked.

"Perhaps, if I can manage the rent." His mother spoke with confidence, although she had only a dollar and a half in her pocket.

The owner of the house happened to be standing nearby. He overheard the conversation and walked up to her. "Are you interested in renting this house?" he asked.

"Are you the owner?" asked Mrs. Bethune.

"Yes, I am, and I'm looking for a renter," replied the man. "You look neat and respectable, better than most folks who rent houses here. I'd like to have you for a tenant."

"How much rent do you want?" Mrs. Bethune asked in her rich, cultivated voice.

Her correct English and way of speaking attracted the owner. "Are you quite sure you want to live in this neighborhood?" he asked. "Somehow you don't seem to belong here."

"Yes, this is exactly where I want to live," replied Mrs. Bethune. "In addition, I want to start a school here."

"What kind of school?" asked the man.

"A school for Negro girls from the homes around here," explained Mrs. Bethune. "These Negro girls here need an opportunity to go to school and to learn how to live and to work."

"You don't know the Negroes here," said the

176

man. "They won't send their children to school. Besides, the Negro children here don't need an education to help them live."

"Well, I disagree," said Mrs. Bethune. "Let's talk more about the house. How much rent are you asking per month?"

The man told her, and Mrs. Bethune turned away. "That's too much," she said.

"Wait a minute," called the owner. "I'll let you have the house for eleven dollars a month, payable in advance."

Mrs. Bethune looked the man straight in the eye. "I don't have eleven dollars, but I'll take the house, starting the first of the month. I'll pay you when I move in."

"All right," said the man. "I wish you good luck, but I think you are crazy to start a school for Negroes here. Your plan won't work."

"Others have told me the same thing," said Mrs. Bethune, "but I have made up my mind. I'm going to start a school in your house, right here in this neighborhood."

"Don't you want to see the inside of the house before you leave?" asked the man.

"Yes, I'll take my son in with me to look around," she replied.

Mrs. Bethune took Albert's hand and started to walk toward the house. "Where can you get the money for rent?" asked Albert.

"I'll earn it somehow, my son. For one thing, I can make sweet potato pies to sell to the workers. Sweet potatoes don't cost much."

They stepped onto the sagging porch of the house, opened the front door, and walked inside. They found two bare rooms and a stairway that led to two empty rooms upstairs. They climbed the rickety steps to the second floor. "This stairway is far different from the first stairway I ever climbed!" Mrs. Bethune said to Albert. "That first stairway was in Scotia Seminary in Con-

178

cord, North Carolina, where I went to school. It seemed almost like a stairway leading up to heaven!"

They looked about the ugly, barren rooms at the head of the stairway. "When we clean these rooms and paint the walls, they will be fine. We'll hold school in the front room downstairs and sleep up here. There's a heap of work to be done, but we can do it."

A few weeks later, Mrs. Bethune stood on the front porch to open her new school. She rang a little silver handbell which a parson at one of the Negro churches had given her. Five little Negro girls and Albert came running, and she welcomed each child with a special word as she led the way into the house.

All the while she whispered a prayer of thanks for this wonderful opportunity. "At last I have set my feet on the path they were meant to follow. My school has begun."

Mrs. Bethune selected a high-sounding name for her unpretentious school. She called it the Daytona Educational and Industrial Training School for Negro Girls. This impressive name merely expressed her feeling of respect for the importance of her undertaking.

The children filed sedately into the front room which was used as a classroom. They took their places on seats made of empty boxes which Mrs. Bethune had found on the dump or begged from nearby stores. The teacher fared no better. Her desk was a packing box and her chair was an upended barrel.

The back room of the house was used as a kitchen and dining room. Mrs. Bethune had furnished it with a makeshift table and with stools. She had found cracked dishes behind some of the hotels and had begged tin pans and kettles from sympathetic white women.

"Children," Mrs. Bethune said, standing be-

fore her pupils, "The Daytona Educational and Industrial Training School for Negro Girls will begin with prayer."

She asked the six sober and impressed children to stand and repeat the Lord's prayer. Then she led them in singing a hymn which was familiar to Negro children and which she thought was particularly suited to the day.

"All glory, laud and honor
To the Redeemer, King!
To whom the lips of children
Make sweet hosannas ring."

The pupils were attracted by Mrs. Bethune's beautiful voice as she led the singing. "Oh Lord!" she prayed silently, "let me do the things I want to do for these children. Bring others, because I feel that I can be an instrument in Your hands to help my people."

Friend of
Presidents

On a november evening in 1949, seventy-four-year-old Dr. Mary McLeod Bethune put on a beautiful, long black-velvet gown. By now she was known as Dr. Bethune because several important universities had bestowed honorary degrees upon her. On her chest she wore the brilliant gold Cross of Haiti, which had been awarded to her earlier by the Republic of Haiti for her work on behalf of Negroes. Her snow-white hair was swept up into a pompadour.

"I never used to care what I wore," Mrs. Bethune explained to a friend who was waiting to take her to the auditorium in Washington, D.C., "but tonight is different. I must look my best because I'll be on television. People all over the country will be looking at me and listening while I speak. How my poor old grandmother would have praised the Lord if she could have lived to see me tonight."

"Not just people of this country will be watching and listening," her friend said, "but people everywhere. Your speech will be broadcast over the Voice of America."

"Yes, I know," said Mrs. Bethune, "and I'm very proud. Here I am, a Negro, speaking to the world as the Voice of America!"

This was the last evening of a three-day convention of the National Council of Negro Women, an organization which Dr. Bethune had founded in 1935. She was president of the organization, and tonight she would hand the gavel over to another noted Negro woman.

The theme of the convention was "World Citizenship through Human Understanding," and Dr. Bethune had decided to speak on the Declaration of Human Rights. She had helped to formulate this Declaration four years earlier when she was a delegate to the United Nations Conference in San Francisco, California.

"That was a wonderful time," she said to her friend, "a time of hope for world peace through the cooperation of all nations."

"Yes, it certainly was," said her friend, "and I know what you did for dark-skinned people then and what you have done since. I remember what you said then and have repeated so many times since, 'I speak for people of all races and creeds who expect the new world to mean something better for them.'"

On the evening of the broadcast a large audience assembled in the auditorium and eagerly awaited Dr. Bethune's arrival. When she entered the great auditorium, the audience burst into a salvo of applause. She walked in a sprightly manner, carrying a beautiful carved cane which barely touched the carpet.

Through the years she had formed a habit of carrying a cane, not because she needed one, but because she used a cane as a trademark. In fact, she had a large collection of canes which prominent people of many countries had given her. The cane which she carried this evening had been used by President Franklin D. Roosevelt. The Roosevelt family had given it to her as a memento of friendship and cooperation in helping the Negroes of America.

When Dr. Bethune mounted the steps to the speakers' platform, several distinguished individuals came over to greet her, including President Harry S. Truman and other leaders of the political, social, and economic world. Then everybody found a seat on the platform and the meeting was ready to begin.

Soon a man stepped forward to introduce Dr. Bethune, the main speaker of the evening. His introduction was very lengthy as he tried to outline the years of service she had given to her country and her people.

First he explained her educational contributions, how she had started a school at Daytona Beach, Florida, with only a dollar and fifty cents in her pocket. He told how by sheer determination and work she had built this school into one of the finest colleges of the country, now known as the Bethune-Cookman Institute.

"When it came to helping her people," the man continued, "she was not too proud to work hard to earn money. She was not too proud to beg from the wealthy visitors who came to the city. Many of these people contributed bountifully to her school. Through these efforts she has helped hundreds, yes, thousands, of young Negroes to lead successful lives."

The speaker went on to explain the services which Dr. Bethune had rendered her country. He mentioned the several government positions she had held. He related how she had traveled thousands of miles each year to study the condition of American Negroes and to encourage them to hope for better ways of living. He told how she had advised Presidents Herbert Hoover, Franklin D. Roosevelt, and Harry S. Truman.

"All these Presidents have considered her not only an authority on Negro affairs, not only a great humanitarian, but also a loyal friend," the man went on. "Her work has been recognized by universities and organizations all over the world. She has been awarded medals never before given to a woman. Without doubt, she is the greatest Negro woman of her time!"

When the man ended his glowing tribute, the entire audience rose to applaud his words. Dr. Bethune was visibly moved by this standing ovation. She found it difficult to get control of her voice to begin her address.

Once she had regained her composure, she spoke in a vibrant tone of voice. She manifested the same spirit that had carried her from the cabin of freed slaves to a place among the elite. She gave an inspiring appeal to the people of the world for human understanding of all races and creeds. She asked for an understanding of the forlorn and the lost, of the neglected and the hopeless, wherever they lived.

When she finished, the audience again stood and provided deafening applause. She stood erect, smiling and gracious, acknowledging the tribute, but at the same time manifesting humility. Somehow her whole attitude seemed to say, "Give the praise to the Lord, where it is due. I have been only an instrument in His hands."

By now she was tired from the strain of the evening, but she stood, smiling, saying words of appreciation, while the great and the humble gathered around to shake her hand. Then, after the crowd slowly departed, she slipped quietly away with her friends. This had been the greatest evening of her life.

Dr. Bethune lived in a house, called "The Retreat," which she had built among the trees on the campus of the Bethune-Cookman Institute. She had a special affection for her study, with its walls of windows. "These are real glass," she would say, smiling as she remembered how she had once asked, "Why can white folks have glass windows when we can't?"

The study was filled with mementos of her busy, active life. On the walls there were photographs of great men and women whom she had met and framed honorary diplomas which she had received. Scattered here and there were her canes, and arranged neatly on tables were miniature elephants of ivory, jade and wood, which

she had long collected. Assembling miniature elephants had started with a gift from a pupil and had become a restful hobby.

In her later years, Mrs. Bethune suffered several illnesses and surgical operations which kept her from carrying on strenuous activities. Following her famous speech as the Voice of America in Washington, D.C., she gave up many of her normal activities and spent more and more time at home.

About a year after her Washington visit, she traveled to New York where important persons gathered to celebrate her seventy-fifth birthday. Many speeches were delivered and many beautiful gifts were showered upon her.

Mary McLeod Bethune lived several more years. When she died in 1955, she was mourned throughout the world for her missionary zeal to help others find ways to better living, regardless of race, color, or creed.

192

More About This Book

WHEN MARY McLEOD BETHUNE LIVED

1875   MARY JANE McLEOD WAS BORN JULY 10 ON A FARM NEAR MAYESVILLE, SOUTH CAROLINA.

Ulysses S. Grant was President.

There were thirty-seven states in the Union.

The population of the country was about 38,560,000.

1875–   MARY JANE GREW UP, OBTAINED AN EDUCATION,
1904   AND BECAME A TEACHER.

Thomas A. Edison invented the phonograph, 1878, and the electric light bulb, 1879.

James A. Garfield was assassinated and Chester A. Arthur became President, 1881.

The American Federation of Labor was organized, 1886.

Thomas A. Edison invented the motion picture camera, 1889.

Henry Ford built his first gas engine, 1893, and first automobile, 1896.

The Spanish-American War was fought, 1898.

193

1904–1933	MRS. BETHUNE FOUNDED A SCHOOL AND LATER BECAME A COLLEGE PRESIDENT.

Robert Peary headed an expedition northward and discovered the North Pole, 1909.

World War I was fought, 1914-1918.

Regular radio broadcasts were begun, 1920.

Stock market prices crashed, and a serious business depression followed, 1929.

1933–1942	MRS. BETHUNE DID WELFARE WORK FOR THE UNITED STATES GOVERNMENT.

Wiley Post flew a small airplane around the world, 1933.

Regular airplane flights were started across the Atlantic Ocean, 1939.

World War II began in 1939, and the United States entered the war, 1941.

1942–1955	MRS. BETHUNE CONTINUED TO SERVE HER PEOPLE AND RECEIVED MANY HONORS.

The United Nations Charter was adopted, 1945.

World War II ended, 1945.

The North Atlantic Treaty Organization was established, 1949.

The Korean War was fought, 1950-1953.

1955   DR. MARY McLEOD BETHUNE DIED AT DAYTONA
BEACH, FLORIDA, MAY 18.

Dwight D. Eisenhower was President.

There were forty-eight states in the Union.

The population of the country was about 150,690,000.

DO YOU REMEMBER?

1. How did Mary Jane manage to have a birthday party for herself?

2. What happened when Mary Jane found a snake in the cotton field?

3. How did Mary Jane first develop a desire to learn how to read?

4. What happened the night of the camp meeting in the yard at the McLeod home?

5. How did Mary Jane get an opportunity to attend a new school for Negro children?

6. Why was Mary Jane disturbed when her father took the cotton to the cotton gin?

7. How did Mary Jane get a new slate to use when she started to school?

8. What new game did Mary Jane teach the small children at school?

6. How was Mary Jane promoted during her first year at school?

10. How did Mary Jane help to check the weight of the family cotton crop at the cotton gin?

11. What did Mary Jane want especially when she graduated from Mayesville Institute?

12. How did Mary Jane continue her education and how did she start her teaching career?

13. How did Mrs. Bethune manage to start a school of her own in Daytona Beach, Florida?

14. How was Dr. Mary McLeod Bethune honored in the later years of her life?

IT'S FUN TO LOOK UP THESE THINGS

1. How did most Negroes in the South make a living after the War between the States?

2. Why was it difficult for many Negro children to attend school?

3. What special training did students obtain at Moody Bible Institute in Chicago?

4. What other Negro educators lived at about the same time as Mary McLeod Bethune?

5. Why was Mary McLeod Bethune selected for an important government position?

6. What significant types of training are provided at Bethune-Cookman College today?

INTERESTING THINGS YOU CAN DO

1. Draw a map to show approximately where Mary McLeod Bethune was born.

2. Explain how most Negro families lived at the time she was born.

3. Find out which amendment to the Constitution gives Negroes the right to vote.

4. Explain the meaning of the term "civil rights" and how it affects Negroes today.

5. Name several colleges and universities that are attended largely by Negroes.

6. Make a list of Negroes who hold important government positions today.

7. Prepare a report on the important contributions of Negroes to science, literature, or music.

OTHER BOOKS YOU MAY ENJOY READING

Booker T. Washington: Ambitious Boy, Augusta Stevenson. Trade and School Editions, Bobbs-Merrill.

Martin Luther King: Boy with a Dream, Dharathula Millender. Trade and School Editions, Bobbs-Merrill.

Mary McLeod Bethune, Catherine Owens Peare. Vanguard.

Mary McLeod Bethune, Emma Gelders Sterne. Knopf.

Prudence Crandall: Woman of Courage, Elizabeth Yates. Dutton.

Story of the Negro, Arna Bontemps. Knopf.

INTERESTING WORDS IN THIS BOOK

apportioned (ă pōr′ shŭnd) : divided in fair shares

arbutus (är bū′ tŭs) : flowering plant that blooms in early spring

assurance (ă shŏŏr′ ăns) : certainty, confidence

balmy (bäm′ ĭ) : mild, pleasant

bolls (bōlz) : rounded pods of a cotton plant which contain both seeds and cotton

brogans (brō′ gănz) : heavy shoes

cipher (sī′ fẽr) : work problems in arithmetic

198

collards (kŏl′ ērdz) : vegetable resembling kale, also known as skunk cabbage

deft (dĕft) : skillful

elite (ȧ lēt′) : choice or best part

emancipation (ė măn′ sĭ pā′ shŭn) : act of freeing, as the slaves in 1863

engrossed (ĕn grōst′) : absorbed, fully occupied

exalted (ĕg zôl′ tĕd) : uplifted

fatback (făt′ băk′) : strip of fat from the back of a hog, cured like bacon

ferocious (fė rō′ shŭs) : fierce, cruel

fervor (fûr′ vēr) : warmth of feeling

flounced (flounst) : moved with an angry or impatient movement of the body

forage (fôr′ ĭj) : search for food

formulate (fôr′ mū lāt) : state or present in systematic form

heathen (hē thĕn) : person who does not believe in the God of Christianity

hepaticas (hė păt′ ĭ kȧz) : delicate blue, pink, purplish, or white spring flowers

humanitarian (hū măn′ ĭ târ′ ĭ ăn) : person who seeks to help mankind

interspersed (ĭn tēr spûrst′) : set or placed here and there

199

itinerant (ī tĭn′ ẽr ănt) : traveling

mementos (mē̇ mĕn′ tōz) : objects treasured for the sake of sentiment or memory, souvenirs

mortgage (môr′ gĭj) : claim on property given in recognition of a debt

mutilated (mū′ tĭ lā′ tĕd) : seriously injured by cutting or tearing

pell-mell (pĕl′ mĕl′) : headlong, in great haste

pompadour (pŏm′ pȧ dōr) : style of wearing the hair combed straight back and high

ravenous (răv′ ĕn ŭs) : greedy, very hungry

rickety (rĭk′ ĕ tĭ) : shaky, tottering

slithering (slĭth′ ẽr ĭng) : sliding about

sorghum (sôr′ gŭm) : syrup made from grain sorghum

sponsors (spŏn′ sẽrz) : persons who are responsible for an organization or group

tension (tĕn′ shŭn) : nervous strain, anxiety

traipse (trāps) : walk or wander slowly

unpretentious (ŭn prē̇ tĕn′ shŭs) : not impressive or showy, modest

vibrant (vī′ brănt) : resounding, vigorous

weevils (wē′ vĭlz) : insects whose larvae eat and destroy cotton

200